Children Learning Science

Children Learning Science

Lyn Sylvester Bradley

Nash Pollock
Publishing

© 1996 Lyn Sylvester Bradley

First published in 1996 by
Nash Pollock Publishing
32 Warwick Street
Oxford OX4 1SX

9 8 7 6 5 4 3 2 1

Orders to:
9 Carlton Close
Grove
Wantage
Oxfordshire OX12 0PU

The author's moral right is asserted.

A catalogue record of this book is available from the British Library.

ISBN 1 898255 08 3

Typeset in 10.5/13 pt New Century Schoolbook, by Can Do Design, Buckingham.

Printed in Great Britain by Redwood Books, Trowbridge

Contents *Summaries*

Acknowledgements

My special thanks go to the many children and teachers whose work I have either mentioned or included.

I would also like to thank:

Leone Burton, for the advice she gave during the writing and editing of the manuscript

Peter Murby, for the encouragement and advice he gave during the initial stages of writing

James Nash, for his help with editing and without whom this book would not have been published

Malcolm Ward, for his invaluable support and encouragement over many years.

Lyn Bradley

Primary Matters: Editors' Preface

It is hard to find an acknowledgement of how recent are primary schools whose curriculum and management reflect the particular emotional, social, intellectual and physical needs of young children, nor of how far they have developed in a very brief time span. Indeed, there are teachers in today's primary schools who remember that in 1949, five years after the famous Butler Education Act, 36% of children of secondary age were still attending schools which also housed children under 11. Those same teachers have seen the development of primary schools through the Plowden era in the 1960s, the building of open-plan schools which aroused such intense international interest in the 1960s and 70s, and the 1980s and the 1988 Education Reform Act.

This Act made far-reaching changes. The introduction of a national curriculum was a radical development and brought in its wake consequences unforseen by its designers. Teachers were quick to discover that the syllabi which had been constructed in such detail were impossible to build into an effective curriculum; tests for 7 and 11 year olds which had been devised to give the curriculum credibility became a focus for parental and professional discontent. Persistent re-writes led finally to a 'reform' of the new curriculum by the Dearing Committee in the early 1990s. This was an attempt to make manageable what was unmanageable, hastily introduced and overburdened with bureaucracy.

These recent changes and upheavals must be set against the slow emergence of a realisation that the needs and aspirations of young people are not necessarily the same at 7 as they are at 13, and that the way in which knowledge is acquired and becomes useful must relate to particular phases in personal development and rhythms of growth.

In the years following the first world war, successive Government committees examined the educational needs of adolescents, of boys and girls in the middle years of childhood (7-11) and of children of infant and nursery age. These committees reported between 1926 and 1933 and their recommendations, though implemented in a piecemeal fashion, did lead to a considerable restructuring of schooling in England and Wales. The most profound effect of these changes was the acknowledgement that the primary years were a coherent and essential stage in the education process, and a stage which had distinctive needs and requirements. Before this children had been educated in all-age schools. Unless a child was fortunate to be selected at the age of 11 (usually as a successful outcome of academic competition), the school s/he joined at 5 years of age would be the school s/he left at 13. 90% of the school population attended such schools and it became increasingly obvious that they were failing to meet the different needs of the 5 year old, the child in middle years, and of the 13 year old school leaver. In the late `1930s primary schools began to develop, with secondary (elementary) schools providing for those children who failed the selective examination. The distinctive categories of secondary education were enshrined in the 1944 Education Act which established a comprehensive tri-partite system of secondary education, but even five years later this was still not fully realised.

It took, therefore, some twenty years from the mid-1930s until the 1950s and 60s for primary schools to become generally established and, with the population explosion of the 50s and 60s, primary school practice underwent many developments as the early years of schooling came to be regarded as an essential phase in the educational process. Experiments were undertaken in teaching and learning methodology, in the curriculum, in the organisation of classes (remember vertical or family grouping?), and, as already mentioned, in the architectural style of new schools. The curriculum became richer and more challenging to young children. Enthusiastic support for these changes was found in the report published by the Plowden Committee in 1967.

In contrast to this period, more recently primary education has been subject to critical appraisal and retrenchment. Academics (like Peters and Dearden), and politicians (like Boyson and Cox), as well as inspectors from local education authorities and Her Majesty's Inspectorate, and more recently the Office for Standards in Education (OFSTED) have focused attention upon the issues and assumptions underlying the work offered by teachers to young children. Are there things which *all* children should learn during their primary years? What constitutes essential knowledge for the primary-age child? What should be the balance between the teaching of facts, the development of skills, the understanding of the concepts which underlie knowledge, and the processes through which this knowledge is acquired and developed? How effective are different classroom approaches in developing thinking skills, social awareness and responsibility? How can the primary curriculum best address the fundamental technological changes brought about by the microchip? In what ways are social issues such as racism, sexism or disadvantage best addressed? How should the particular insights and experiences of the disabled child be incorporated? How can institutional barriers to the involvement of all interested parties, especially parents, in the education of each child be dismantled? How should religious education be handled within a society which is more and more secular but also no longer made up of only one major faith group?

Questions such as these are not asked in a vacuum. They reflect the anxieties (real and imagined) of parents, academics, politicians, employers, and, most of all, of the teachers themselves. That such questions are now being asked is, in part, a recognition of how far primary schools have come over the fifty or so years since they were first conceived. In a climate of concern and criticism, it is also easy to forget that British developments in primary education have been the focus of attention, respect and emulation in many other countries. Indeed, many have argued that it was a freedom from bureaucracy which gave English primary schools their unique character and made possible the kinds of thoughtful experiment which attracted an international reputation. At the same time, others have suggested that piecemeal development has led to idiosyncrasy. Hence the current demand for every school to follow a programme reflecting clearly defined national criteria. However, the need for the individual teacher to make choices, ask questions, and influence every child's development continues to be respected and, however centralised the curriculum may become, however much the school programme is evaluated, however regularly children are tested against performance norms, the thoughtful teacher will continue to ask questions about *what* John or Akbar, Mary or Mai-Lin will learn, how they will learn it, what particular needs they have and how their individual interests, attitudes and aptitudes can be accommodated into and contribute to the daily work of the classroom.

As we have already noted the national curriculum has undergone considerable changes since its implementation. Nevertheless it remains a reference point around which head teachers and subject co-ordinators construct the school experience offered to their pupils, a situation which is unlikely to change whatever party is in government. But the teacher is not powerless. The curriculum of a school has rightly been defied as 'everything that happens in a school day but leaves undefined the meanings which are constructed and attributed by the pupils'. Such definitions tend to embrace the content (the 'what'), the approaches to unspoken attitudes (the 'how'), and the learning strongly influenced by beliefs which underpin the relationship between school, home and community (the 'why'). The content (what should schools teach?) is the least difficult of these diverse elements to measure, although we have already noted the difficulties encountered by the national curriculum exercise. But what young people will learn by engaging with the content is not only problematic but a source of persistent questioning by effective teachers. The titles in this series acknowledge the centrality of subjects in any national curriculum but at the same time seek to show the many ways in which a prescribed curriculum can be vivified and enriched.

All the books in this series address aspects of the kinds of questions which teachers are asking as part of their concern to establish effective strategies for learning. Part of that concern focuses upon the links between the excitement of learning evidenced by young children, and the need to evaluate and maintain coherence in their experiences. Effective learning is the product of engagement as each member of the group struggles to make the learning process his or her own. At the same time, personal learning can still be limited unless it is placed in a broader context so that, for example, subject strands unite into a comprehensible and rational whole. Each author in this series seeks to indicate cross-curricular links, even though the titles indicate particular subject specialisms as starting points, so that the approach unifies rather than divides the child's experience of the curriculum.

As editors of this series, we wish to offer practising primary teachers a range of titles which recognises the complexity of the primary teacher's role. Each book gives shape and purpose to a specific curriculum area, dealing with issues which are particular to that specialism, presenting ideas for interesting and innovative practice in that area but, at the same time, emphasising the unity of the primary experience. Thus, each title is set against a broad canvas, that of the primary school as a living and vibrant place in which young children grow and learn.

Leone Burton

Henry Pluckrose

1   Learning science informally

*There remains the question of education, usually a subject for
snobs or fanatics. But I would like to give her the sort that
matches her curiosity and needs, and not one to make her life
a misery. May spontaneity and warmth be her main
achievements, not gradings in academic abstractions. May she
feel confident, wanted, take pleasure and give it, be artful (but
not want to act), laugh easily, covet no one, forget herself
sometimes, never be bored or feel the need to kill time, avoid
painting-by-numbers, processed food, processed language,
have an antenna for the responses of others, and learn that
though animals are often much easier to love than men (and
both worth it) loving man needs more talent...*

Laurie Lee, *I Can't Stay Long*

From a very early age, children have a wonder, curiosity and
excitement about the world around them. Young babies are attracted
to the unknown and unfamiliar and are naturally inquisitive. They
want to learn about their world and are very energetic, resourceful,
adaptive and inventive in exploring and finding out about it. Very
young children are capable of spending long hours happily and
productively and are by nature independent and self-directing
learners, who are often extremely determined to learn about the
things that they find of interest. They take pride in doing this, as
they enjoy learning about their discoveries and in satisfying their
curiosity. They are serious, purposeful and eager to learn, with a
desire for mastery and competence.

In the process of growing up some part of this eagerness and
aliveness is given up or destroyed. This personal alienation is
caused, in part, by structuring so much of their time for them. From
an early age, much of most children's time is completely organised

and supervised – play time, television time, bath time, story time and so on. Children gradually become passive participants in structuring their own time. Invariably when children complain of being 'bored' or having nothing to do, it is because they are so conditioned to having their time planned for them that they are no longer able to rely on their own resources. Many infant teachers are familiar with children who are unable to 'choose' and who wander aimlessly around the classroom with no real interest. This may be because the children are so used to being told what to do and when to do it, that they are adrift in this new freedom, or it may be that the activities that are made available are 'boring' because they are not of importance or interest to the children at that time. Trying to interest children in activities for which they are not ready or for which they do not see a need invariably leads to little real understanding and may also destroy their joy of learning.

Children are people and as such have a right to decide for themselves what they consider worth thinking about. There are so many things in the world that could be learned, and yet adults not only frequently deny children the right to make their own selections, but also manage to imply that children's interests are not ones that are really worth thinking about. By choosing for them, we discourage children from making up their own minds, drawing their own conclusions, thinking up questions that are important to them and finding ways to get useful answers. Their interests, like ours, will change with time; but they do know what they want to find out about and are eager to learn. When activities are of real importance to the children we no longer have artificially to stimulate their interest and encourage their endeavours. Interested learners quickly acquire the skills and knowledge that they want to use. The nine year old who develops a passion for fishing will go to great lengths to find out about different types of fish, their characteristics and habitats, as well as learning the practicalities of the sport, and will soon be far more knowledgeable on the subject than the average primary school teacher.

As teachers we need to capitalise on that energy and purpose. Whilst this may not always be possible within the confines of the curriculum, we can at least ensure that some time is set aside for the children to choose their own activities and work at their own pace so that they can 'lose themselves' in exploring their own areas of interest. Children who have the freedom to design their own work and their own working pattern also tend to structure their own learning. We can encourage them to do this by providing:

- access to people, places and things
- assistance and resources to make it easier for them to find out what they want to find out (not what we think they ought to find out)
- plenty of time and space in which they can think over and compare their experiences by themselves
- opportunities to use those experiences creatively and reflect upon them in order to make them meaningful.

Pre-school experiences of science

Children are learning all day long as they go about their own business. Parents sometimes underestimate the contribution that people, places, the home and the family make to their children's intellectual, social and emotional development, and can give the impression to their children that anything learned outside school is not of as much value as the teaching that they receive in school. Yet the children's daily experiences contribute to their ideas and to the interpretations and explanations which they make about the world around them. Although their ideas may not necessarily accord with adult thinking, they will make sense to the children. Some of these everyday activities will have enabled all children to have learnt some science before they start compulsory schooling. They (and their parents) may not recognise their ideas as scientific ones, but they will undoubtedly have ideas about the world around them and how and why it works. Before he started school, four year old Simon explained his idea about why it rains:

It rains because the sun shines on the tops of the clouds and pushes the rain out and it rains down on us.

From an early age much of the children's scientific learning will have come from the varied environment in and around their homes, the sharing of information and demonstrating of skills by parents and other close adults. The children may also acquire ideas through:

- parents passing on their expectations and fears (possibly without realising it) – "Tommy's going to be a doctor like his Daddy when he grows up."
- being told or shown how to do things or being encouraged to have a go at doing things for themselves (over and over again if necessary) – "Make sure the hole is big enough for the roots to be able to spread out."
- being given plenty of time to assimilate or practise their new knowledge or skills and then, when they are ready, being

provided with more – "Shall we make buns this time when Grandad comes?"

- being encouraged to ask questions and to try to find answers to them – "See if you can find a picture in the bird book that shows the difference."

- being given feedback so that they can find out how well they are doing and thus improve their performance – "Next time it might be a good idea not to put quite such a lot of oil on the chain, then most of it won't come off on your socks."

Children often have an innate understanding of science that they have acquired by physically using scientific principles in their play long before they come face to face with them in their formal education. This common sense science can be observed, for instance, in any playground when watching children using a see-saw. While they may not be able to verbalise their understanding of levers in terms of the physics involved, they can explain that by pushing up one end of the see-saw they can make the other end go down. They know that it pivots in the middle and that they can balance people sitting on either side of the pivot by wriggling up and down the length of the see-saw. Such play experiences can later be capitalised on in science lessons.

'That's what schools are for'

There is no one 'right' way to teach, and most teachers use a variety of methods throughout each day. Children learn in many different ways, and the best one is that which excites, interests and satisfies them at that moment. Unfortunately parents sometimes believe that learning refers only to the development of academic skills and that such learning can only happen in school. "He learns about books and arithmetic in school. We haven't got time to teach him. That's what schools are for." Yet the average child speaks seventeen words a day to the class at large and receives at the most fifteen minutes of individualised teaching a week. Many children may receive only commands, correction, warnings or blame rather than actual teaching. What children learn formally in school is only a very small part of their total learning, as most of the children's learning is informal and much of it takes place outside school. If school learning makes sense and fits into the pattern of the children's lives outside school then such learning is far more effective, as anything that isolates the school from their environment can cause children to reject any teaching that they receive there.

Many parents do not distinguish between learning and schooling. They therefore believe that their children go to school in order to be taught and to learn and that teaching and learning happens only in school by the serious business of 'doing work'. Parents expect the teacher to teach their children formally in order to make them learn. Children on starting school, very quickly come to expect the teacher to teach them something by making them 'do work'. If they decide that learning means being taught only by 'the teacher', they will be less likely to want or feel able to explore and make sense of the world around them in their own way and for their own reasons. Thus they may not only have their original imagination destroyed by the socialising process, but may also fail to maximise their own potential. Children too often reach a required standard, set for them, at which their performance is satisfactory, and unless they manage to retain the ability to make demands of themselves they will rarely go beyond such limits.

Learning science from other children

Children are often encouraged not to help each other with their school work. Yet learning results from communicating, comparing and contrasting ideas and understandings. Many children are good at helping others to learn, as they tend to be direct and are often blunt and to the point. Children often find it easier to tell another child, rather than an adult (especially if that adult is the teacher), that they do not know or are in a muddle about something. Unlike the children's relationship with their teacher, the teaching/learning relationship between children is not compulsory and is usually only a temporary one. Children generally want to please their teachers, and by confessing their ignorance or saying that they have a problem children sometimes worry that they will disappoint the teacher or that they will be given a bad mark as a result. Asking another child to help does not involve disappointment or marks. A child who asks another to help him learn something invariably chooses one who he thinks knows and if for some reason the chosen child does not know or can not manage to help him, then the learner will find a different child and no kudos will be lost.

Luigi, aged eight, asked nine year old Robin to help him understand about batteries.

Robin: *Look, it doesn't matter how big the battery is. It's what's in them what matters.*

Luigi: *What's in them?*

Robin: *Yea. A battery's got chemicals in it. It stores energy. Energy that makes things go. Look.* (He picks up a battery and points to the voltage marked on it.) *See. It's 1.5 volts. The size doesn't matter. Look at this one.* (He picks up a smaller sized battery also of 1.5 volts.) *This one's 1.5 volts too but it's smaller. It goes in one of them tiny torches. This one's bigger, it goes in a big torch that's all. It makes the big torch work. Now, what's this one?* (He picks up a larger 1.5 volt battery.)

Luigi: *1.5 volts.*

Robin: *Yea. It's the same volts as the other ones but it's not the same size. O K, now supposing you want a lot of energy to make something big go. What battery do you want?*

Luigi: *One with lots of volts.*

Robin: *Right! Now, if you haven't got a battery with enough volts, you can use more than one battery so's you can get enough volts. You can add them up. What've we got here? Add them up.*

Luigi: *4.5 volts.*

Robin then proceeded to demonstrate how the batteries could be connected either in series or in parallel and continued to explain the difference between the two types of circuits until Luigi understood. Although Luigi had realised that batteries 'made things go', he had not considered them as sources of energy and that the energy they provided would be distributed differently in series and parallel circuits. Robin was clear about this and was able to express it in a way that enabled Luigi to understand.

Working together provides children with opportunities to explore and clarify their ideas and to help each other to work towards a greater understanding. In a class of six year olds two girls were working together on a simple electrical circuit consisting of a battery connected to a light bulb. Their teacher asked them why they thought a circuit had to be complete in order to work. Amy and Mary together explored their understanding of circuits as they compared their ideas.

Amy: *If we break the circuit...*

Mary: *The light goes out.*

Amy: *Why does the light go out?*

Mary: *Because we broke the circuit.*

Amy: *Yes, but why doesn't the light work when the circuit's broken?*

Mary: *Because... the break stops it working somehow.*

Amy: *The break stops the light working. But the battery makes the light work, 'cos when we got that dud battery the light wouldn't work.*

Mary: *Something in the battery makes the light work.*

Amy: *Well, if something in the battery makes the light work, it's got to go down this wire to get there* (she points to one of the wires connecting the battery to the bulb) *and if we pull this wire out it can't get there and the light doesn't work.*

Mary: *Yes, but if we pull the other wire out it don't work either. So it might be going down this wire to the light.* (She points to the other wire connecting the battery to the bulb.)

Amy: *P'raps it goes down both wires to the light.*

At this point their teacher intervened and suggested that they looked carefully at the battery. Once they had noticed the + sign by the positive terminal and the − sign by the negative terminal, the teacher was able to suggest that they got two batteries and tried connecting them positive to negative, positive to positive and negative to negative, thus helping the girls to find out about the direction of flow of electricity around the circuit.

Of course, scientific misconceptions can be learnt as easily as 'correct' ideas, irrespective of whether it is the teacher, a parent or another child who is doing the teaching. Parents and teachers, as well as children, may hold inaccurate or only partially formed concepts; and until such concepts are challenged or examined we may not even realise that we hold some that are unhelpful or incorrect. Indeed there may not even be a rational basis for some of the concepts we unconsciously hold. A phobia about snakes can cause many misconceptions about their structure and behaviour. If all of us can keep an open mind and accept that our scientific understanding is at best only partial and provisional, and that our ideas can be changed in the light of new experiences, and that there is not necessarily a known or a 'right' answer, then we can help each other to overcome misconceptions as and when we become aware of them. Many adults have a fear of not having the 'right' answer, particularly where science is concerned. The ability to admit that you do not know but can try to find out can be a useful lesson to share with the children. This may mean that, on occasion, teachers have to set up experimentation in response to children's questioning as a way of developing their scientific understanding. "I don't know how much the gerbil eats. How could we try to find out?" This book provides examples of many strategies that have been tried and tested in a variety of primary classrooms in response to this type of open-ended approach. By encouraging the children to find out things for themselves and each other, we are also sharing the excitement, joy and value of learning.

Learning science by using symbols

Communication is an imparting or exchange of experience. In order to do this there has to be an experience that gives rise to the need to communicate, an appropriate means of expressing what has to be communicated, and suitable symbols to represent what is to be communicated. From our earliest days we learn to communicate non-verbally, and non-verbal communication remains an important and yet often overlooked aspect of communication. A glance or gesture can so often contradict or strengthen our comments. Recoiling from a spider whilst maintaining that it does not hurt, gives conflicting and confusing messages to others.

Communication takes many forms; and as they grow and develop children gradually become more aware of the variety of ways of communicating and more skilful at handling a range of symbols. As they use and interpret symbols, children also learn to discriminate. When they start school the children quickly become able to differentiate between the teacher's whistle and the school bell. They learn to recognise that both sounds are symbols of command and that they are expected to do something on hearing them. As the children become more able to classify symbols, they begin to realise that not only do the symbols remain constant but that it is also important that they are of an unchanging nature. If the symbol *cm* was sometimes used as a symbol for length and at other times was used as a symbol for mass, "It's 10 cm" would become meaningless.

Many children are aware of some of the meteorological symbols seen daily on the weather forecasts on the television. They often know the meanings of some of them and produce similar symbols themselves when making their own weather charts. Such experiences enable them to associate symbols seen in one context with those seen in another. Thus weather symbols seen on the television can be related to weather symbols in newspapers. Many of the symbols that the children learn informally are necessary to their formal education. As the children learn to interpret such symbols, they become aware that the data associated with them vary and that it is possible to analyse that data and to look for patterns in them.

Learning science by using books

The social, intellectual and emotional development of young children is one of gradual growth interspersed with sudden giant leaps. These abrupt increases may be due to enforced external requirements, such as starting school, or may be due to far less stressful influences, such as a book or television programme that captures their interest and sets the children off on a trail of exploration and discovery. Books and television can both expand the children's interests and raise their awareness of different ideas and values. If these unexpected enthusiasms can be encouraged and focused, we can more effectively help the children to become independent learners and to share their knowledge and ideas with others. We can encourage all the children to talk about their interests to the rest of the group or class and can call on a particular child for specific information. "Ask Dave about that. He knows far more about how motorbike engines work than I do."

The children can all be encouraged to contribute to a list of 'useful books' that they have come across either at school, or at home, or in the local library. They can note the title, author, page numbers (if appropriate) and where the book is to be found, along with a few accompanying words that explain its usefulness.

Title	Author	Publisher	Comment	Place	Signed
The Acid Rain Effect	*Philip Neal*	*Batsford*	*Explains causes + damage to man-made and natural environment and ways of us preventing it. Good colour photos*	*Armley library science section*	*Pat S.*

The list can be referred to when particular information is needed: "Does anyone know where we can find a simple drawing of a human skeleton?" The children are able to benefit from each other's findings and noting the title, author and publisher of a book helps them to realise that such information is important and has to be accurate if anyone one else is to be able to make use of it.

Learning science by using language

Learning is mediated by language and the meanings that we give to words. In learning science we have not only to learn the specialised vocabulary of science but we also have to build up a language that is rich and wide ranging so that we can use it to conceptualise and communicate. Some of our everyday language also has a scientific meaning, and we need to be aware of the difference between the common and scientific meanings of words so that we do not inadvertently cause misunderstandings. Similarly some of our everyday idioms and metaphors, such as 'dying light' and 'as dead as a doornail', may lead to misconceptions by being scientifically inaccurate. While this can be a problem for all children, it is a particular difficulty for any child whose first language is not English.

Children's use of language responds to adult encouragement, and most children delight in learning new words and in trying them out. Acrostics, rhyming words and writing poems are fun ways of developing linguistic awareness and verbal thinking. They can also provide the teacher with a useful insight into the children's understanding of scientific words. Figures 1.1 and 1.2 are examples of an acrostic and a cinquaine about a chrysalis, written collaboratively by two 10 year olds. They demonstrate the girls' understanding of both the word *chrysalis* and the concept of metamorphosis.

Chrysalis
Hanging on a twig
Remembering being a caterpillar
Yearning to be a butterfly.
Soon it will hatch
And then it will
Look for
It's mate
So the cycle can be repeated.

Figure 1.1   An acrostic about a chrysalis

> Chrysalis
> Waiting, longing
> Ugly, dull, unnoticed
> What will it become?
> Butterfly!

Figure 1.2   A cinquaine about a chrysalis

A cinquaine is a short five line poem with a specific structure. The first line is a single word epitomising the substance of the poem, in this case – chrysalis. The second line has two words, both verbs, that express the activity of the poem. The third line has three words, all adjectives describing the activity of the poem. The fourth line is a four word sentence containing the essence of the poem. The fifth line is again a single word that sums up the feeling of the poem. When writing a structured poem of this type children have to be very clear about their use of English (do they know what verbs and adjectives are?) and also about their understanding of the subject matter. This can give the teacher an opportunity to discover any misconceptions or partially formed concepts that the children hold, as well as bringing to light knowledge or skills of which she was unaware.

Learning science by following personal interests

Artefacts can also spark off an interest or enthusiasm in children. Nearly all primary classrooms contain collections of objects that are displayed in such a way that the children can interact with them. Obviously such items have to be displayed with safety considerations in mind and sometimes it will be necessary for things to be protected. However, if the children can have access to such a resource at all times and are able to use it independently of adult supervision, then they will have more opportunities in which to lose themselves in fully exploring an interest. A series of old X-rays of the hands of people aged between 3 months and 69 years was freely available to a class of six year olds. Through looking at them many of the children discovered to their surprise that bones grow and change shape. Some children came back to the X-rays time and time again and spent hours looking at them and moving their own hands in different ways.

They were fascinated by how the number of bones enabled so many different movements of the hand to be possible.

If children are to think through their own ideas and learn with understanding, they need opportunities to choose an object that interests them or an activity that they want to pursue, to look at the object or to repeat the activity time and time again until they are completely satisfied, to explore it at their own pace, and to raise questions about it. Although the activity a child chooses may sometimes appear to us simple or passive, such as repeatedly rolling a ballbearing down a slope or watching the class hamster eating, it is of importance and value to the child who has chosen it.

However, children's perceptions are not necessarily the same as adult ones. Nine year old Jane repeatedly looked at the leaf of a *streptocarpus* through a magnifying glass, before announcing that "The leaf's got hairs on it underneath. They're to catch the water when you water it." The fact that the soil around the plant, not the leaves, was invariably watered was irrelevant to her. The hairs were there for a reason and she believed she had found the reason. By providing her with opportunities to water plants and to look at other plants with hairless leaves, her teacher was able to challenge this idea and help her to reflect on it and modify it.

Many scientific inventions have been brought about because of the investigators' refusal to see things in the same way as other people, and their persistence in investigating them. For example, in the 1860s Joseph Lister revolutionised modern surgery by his introduction of the use of antiseptics. He steadfastly believed that invisible organisms caused the suppuration that nearly always developed in wounds after an operation and so often led to the patient's death. Despite others' disbelief in this germ theory, he used dressings soaked in carbolic acid on all surgical wounds with the result that wound infection was dramatically reduced. By providing the children with opportunities to follow their own interests, and encouraging them to seek explanations, observe closely, and focus on the details that they believe to be important, we can help them to develop as scientists.

Learning through play

Play in the classroom is of necessity limited by the environment, materials, time, contexts and playmates that the children have available to them. One of many disservices that we do to children is to give them the idea that they cannot enjoy themselves without being provided with the proper equipment. Yet, when they show ingenuity and solve the problem of lack of appropriate materials creatively we sometimes tend to disapprove. Thus Janine, aged five, who painstakingly made some beautiful 'cakes' in the sand tray and took them into the Wendy house to share with her 'children', was told by her teacher that the sand belonged in the sand tray and she must go and put it back straight away.

However, much informal school learning is acquired through play and discovery. Play, both structured and unstructured, is a process that provides the children with opportunities for exploration, and allows them to test and re-test their ideas. However, play is sometimes not recognised by parents, teachers of older children, or even children themselves, as a basis for learning. Play is a vital part of the children's development of their social and intellectual skills; and yet in school it is often marginalised and relegated to various activities, toys and games from which children can choose once they have finished their 'work'. If play is always offered as a reward for work or seen as the opposite of work, then it will carry the wrong message and not be regarded as being valuable in its own right. Play is important for children of all ages because it can:

- stimulate them and motivate them to ask questions and rely on their own resources
- allow them to make mistakes without losing face or feeling bad;
- help them to work through problems by pretending or fantasising
- provide opportunities for practising the familiar and learning about the unfamiliar
- stimulate language development and practice
- help them to gain confidence in themselves and their abilities
- allow them to concentrate and become totally involved in what they are doing
- provide opportunities for co-operation
- allow them to express themselves and to be innovative and creative
- be fun and a means of enjoyment and amusement.

Free-play and directed play

Free-play, that is play that is not restricted in any way by others, allows the children to use all their senses to explore the materials provided. During free-play the children are actively investigating and manipulating the materials in order to discover what they can do. As they do so they may restructure their ideas about how something works or fits together. Given a box of unfamiliar construction equipment, children will initially spend time finding out about the different types of pieces, the potential ways in which they can be joined, and the limitations of the shapes and sizes. Many adults when faced with a new gadget or resource do not allow themselves time for this exploratory phase and expect to be able to master the new material competently and immediately and may feel a failure, or dismiss the equipment, if they are unable to do so. In our own childhood, we may have lacked experiences that, if we have not since had opportunities to compensate for them, could cause difficulties for us as teachers. For example, some women when young may not have been allowed to use tools, make things from wood, build electric circuits and so on, as such materials and activities were regarded as inappropriate for girls. If as adults they still have not had the chance actively to investigate and handle these materials, they will feel neither confident nor competent as role models in using resources of this kind, and so the stereotyping of activities that females cannot do will be perpetuated.

This experience of acquiring information is an essential prerequisite of directed play, whether it be directed by the child itself or others. Much directed play in the classroom is organised by the teacher, either overtly or through the resources provided, the activities chosen, the context (office, shop, hospital, etc.) and the approval or disapproval given to the children: "I know full means right up to the top, Jimmy, but it doesn't mean overflowing onto the floor." Repeated contact with different play materials enables the children to attain some degree of mastery in using them. The children are only then able to put into practice the skills and the knowledge that they have gained about the properties of the material, in order to understand what they can (and cannot) do with them. Thus children who have had the opportunity for free-play in the sand will have discovered some of its properties. That knowledge can be built on in directed play by, for example, challenging them to use dry sand to make a device that can measure a specific period of time.

Learning science through play

Sand and water are found in most infant classrooms nowadays and are usually readily accessible to the children. However, they are sometimes not recognised by either parents or children as serious learning media. This is often reinforced by a teacher's direction to "Go and *play* in the sand/water." The discoveries about sand and water that the children make for themselves will be limited by the materials available (types and amounts of sand, water and containers) and the ways in which they are allowed to use them. Damp and wet sands behave in different ways to dry sand and can be used for different purposes and to provide experiences of building, tunnelling and sculpting. By exploring the nature and behaviour of sand and water, the children will find ways in which they can manipulate them and with repetition become skilful at doing so. These experiences can also enhance their language development, as they learn new words such as 'filter' or 'submerge' to express their ideas and learn new meanings for already known words like 'rough' and 'float'.

Children learn as individuals and at their own pace. Their ideas about sand and water develop slowly and depend on their continuing experiences of them. They try things out time and time again to verify their ideas. Six year old David filled a container full of dry sand and then poured it carefully into another differently shaped container, which it also filled. He poured them back and forth several times before announcing, "These two hold the same amount, you know."

If free-play with sand and water is followed by directed play, then the information that the children have acquired about the properties of sand and water can be built on and new experiences provided that will help them towards scientific ideas. For example, there are many different types and grades of sand that vary in both colour and texture, and yet there is often only one type available in the classroom. By providing a magnifying glass and different types of sand (silver sand from a river bank, golden sand from a beach, black volcanic sand or coloured sands from Alum Bay) and a piece of sandstone, we can encourage the children to ask questions and form ideas about the range and origins of sand. Different types of sand will also enable the children to have opportunities to investigate how texture affects the angle of the slope formed when sand is poured and how equal measures of different types of sand have different masses.

At six or seven years of age children are beginning to have ideas about not only *what* happens but *why* it happens. As the children begin to notice that if they do something, something else may happen as a result, they become able to form simple hypotheses that they can test. In order to form a hypothesis, the children must draw on their existing knowledge and observations so that they can put forward an idea that is testable. Following some investigations that they had previously made into the structure of soil, eight year olds Louise and Chris realised that air is trapped between particles of sand and that they could find out how much air was trapped by displacing it with water and measuring the volume of the water used. They used this knowledge to hypothesise that different types of sand with different size grains would trap different amounts of air. However, they were not sure whether finer grains of sand would trap more or less air. By testing their hypothesis on both finer and coarser grained sands they were able to refine their ideas.

By providing the children with opportunities for exploration and allowing them to test and re-test their ideas (rather than ours) in different situations, we can help them to reflect on their ideas and to modify, accept and consolidate them. This can only happen over a period of time and the children's concepts of sand and water will not be complete simply because they have left the infant classroom. Yet opportunities for them to use sand and water and to continue to develop ideas about them are still lacking in most junior classrooms.

Learning science through rule-bound play

Rule-bound play is play that is governed by a set of rules that are known and understood by the players. Play of this type can be carried out alone or with others. Rule-bound play is often of a co-operative or competitive nature, or both, if the children work in pairs or small groups to meet a deadline or target. "We need the light on the top of the lighthouse to flash. I want each group to use the equipment on their table to work out a way of doing it before break. We'll use the best design on our model."

For some rule-bound play co-operation is an essential, as this conversation between two nine year olds shows. Sarah was describing an ivy leaf to Anitra, who could not see the leaf but was attempting to draw it from Sarah's description. This required Sarah to observe closely and to be accurate in her choice of language, while Anitra had to interpret correctly what was being told to her and ask pertinent questions.

Sarah: *It's green and shiny; darker green on the top. There's three points and the point in the middle's longer than the other two. Down the middle of the points is a big vein and off the big veins are small veins. The big veins meet up where the stalk's joined on.*

Anitra: *How big is it?*

Sarah: *Umm. It's a bit smaller than the bottom of the pencil pot, but it's not round. It's sort of heart-shape. The stalk goes where the dippy bit in the heart goes, but the bottom bit's not a proper heart 'cos it's got three points remember.*

Anitra: (draws) *Like this? With the stalk here?*

Sarah: *Sort of, but the two points at the sides aren't as pointy. They're not quite the same. I think it's meant to be symmetrical but it isn't.*

The conversation continued for some fifteen minutes during which time both girls had clearly been motivated. They had found out much about leaf structure by such a close examination of it and Anitra's final drawing of the leaf was a very good representation.

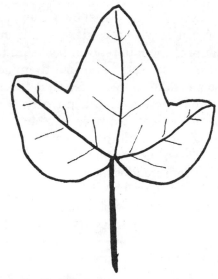

Figure 1.3   Anitra's drawing of an ivy leaf done, without seeing the leaf, by interpreting a description of it

Resources for informal learning

Basic classroom play provision often includes construction kits, painting and drawing equipment, sand, water, clay, home-corner and books. Inevitably some of these play materials tend to encourage product-oriented activities more than others, and this is often reinforced by adult expectation. Children using paper, brush and paint are invariably expected to produce paintings, yet when they spend time in the home-corner a product is not usually expected. If we acknowledge that play is a process, then we also need to recognise that play will not necessarily have any outcome unless those playing want it to have one; and we may have to revise our expectations accordingly.

The resources that we provide for the children need to be carefully considered, as well as the way in which they are stored; and this may have implications for the organisation of the classroom. If they are stored in such a way that all the children have access to them and can choose for themselves the items that they want to use, then the children will have greater freedom to follow their own interests and enthusiasms and to practise their skills and to find out more about the resources as and when they need to do so. Easy access is also more likely to encourage the children to put things away when they have finished with them.

The children may also need to be shown how to look after the resources and care for them with consideration. It may be necessary, for example, to encourage them to respect books and treat them with care, or to carry scissors correctly and use them sensibly. We may also have to help some children to realise that the resources belong to the school and are not there to be taken freely. When teaching the children to value the resources, we may have to emphasise that all the children have a right to use all the items: "Tell the girls they can't play with the bricks, Miss; they're for the boys." From an early age, children seem to have definite ideas about what girls can do and use and what boys can do and use. This is often reinforced by parental expectations of what girls and boys should be doing and using and by the way in which gender identity is regarded in the family. Traditionally adults tend to buy more presents of spatial and scientific toys (construction sets, toy microscopes, chemistry sets, etc.) for boys than girls. Some toy manufacturers have attempted to overcome this bias. For example, in an attempt to make Lego more user-friendly and attractive to girls and to reduce its masculine image, Lego is now also marketed in pastel colours and some sets are based on conventional feminine themes (home, family etc.) that girls supposedly find more acceptable.

Girls also differ from boys in the ways in which they use resources. Whereas boys may sometimes use (or abuse) the equipment in order to show how tough they are, girls will rarely do so. Thus a boy may demonstrate his toughness by using a spring as a catapult to launch paper pellets around the classroom, or a torch as a ray gun. Also, boys are more likely to use the resources to construct something (a rocket to go to the moon, a model with working parts or a garage for a tractor) whereas girls tend to prefer to use the resources to create something (a fantasy about an ill baby, a picture of a dinosaur or a pattern of leaf prints). Even when using the same equipment there is a marked difference in the approach used by the different sexes and the consequent learning that takes place. Boys, for example, tend to use construction toys together, although often competitively, whereas girls often play with them alone. Thus a girl may be seen on her own carefully creating a house, while a group of boys makes trucks and then has races. Given this apparent innate difference in the use of resources, we need to be aware that encouraging the children to use the equipment in a different way or to try an activity that they do not normally choose, does not necessarily ensure that they will actually attempt to do so. Some children will develop strategies in order to avoid doing something that they do not want to do. On being asked to try a different activity, they may for instance immediately move out of the teacher's sight or, conversely, make sure that the teacher notices them sitting and fiddling with the equipment for a few minutes before they move away. Once they are out of sight, they hope that the teacher will forget about them and what they are supposed to be doing.

The particular resources provided will also affect whether the children play with them on their own or with others. Sand and water, for instance, often engender solitary play even when there is a group of children working alongside each other and sharing equipment. A far more social type of play can be seen in, for example, a pretend hospital, when the children play with each other and have to negotiate about different roles and use of the resources. This kind of play also depends on the composition of the group and the subsequent group dynamics. Children's play can be enriched by an adult playing with them as an equal, too, rather than directing the play from the outside. When the children organise the play for themselves they are creating situations that are under their control. The playing adult, therefore, needs to be sensitive to the mood and requirements of the children in order to decide when and how it would be pertinent to intervene and change the play in any way. Play is important for the social and intellectual development of all children, and the learning from it can be maximised if the resources and opportunities provided enable them to experience being able to play alone, alongside others and in pairs, as well as in small groups.

Time for informal learning

The time that we allow children for informal learning through play and discovery is a factor that is sometimes overlooked. The children require time to explore the resources and to become skilful at using them, as well as opportunities to repeat the activities at a later date. Not all children will need the same amount of time for this. Similarly, children who are playing in order to solve a problem or work something through need time to develop their ideas. If we value play as a means of learning and appreciate that all learning is a change that takes place over a period of time, then we should be prepared to allow the children time in which to maximise the learning from their play.

The pressures of time can sometimes cause us to be dismissive about the things the children make when playing, which then gives them the wrong messages about the value and importance of play. "It doesn't matter if you don't finish your tall tower, Kate. Can you get all the straws cleared away before dinner, please?" We often spend time spurring children on to finish a piece of writing or a page of sums; and yet play activities do not merit the same encouragement. Pressures of space can cause similar problems. "Where's the model windmill I made yesterday, Miss?" "It was too big to keep, Pete. It got thrown away." The children know that we would not break up or throw out their 'work' and deduce that something that is disposed of in this way obviously is not 'work' and therefore must be of less value. We often unwittingly reinforce our attitude about values by casual remarks such as, "That paper is for writing, Robbie. Use scrap paper if you want to make paper aeroplanes" and by providing 'good' paper for writing and less good paper for painting.

Pressures of time, as well as the sheer pressure of numbers of children in our classes, can also cause us to overlook the praise and reward we give for informal learning. Children usually expect their efforts to be recognised by a smile, word of approval or other acknowledgement, and, if they do not get the expected reward time after time, they may conclude that their efforts are misplaced or unappreciated. The child who chooses to write a poem or do a detailed drawing of something that excites him and who gets little encouragement or has his efforts dismissed with a brief "Put that away, Jamie. It's packing up time" may lose heart. The lack of such praise and reward, whether it is consciously or unconsciously considered by the children, may affect their informal learning and eventually their behaviour.

Planning for informal learning

Although it is sometimes possible to capitalise on spontaneous opportunities for informal learning, much of it has to be planned for in the same way that we plan for formal learning. The exploratory phase of free-play will not happen unless the children are given opportunities to use resources as they see fit. We cannot expect to foster creativity in children who are continually restricted in what they may or may not do and how they may or may not use equipment. Directed play can encourage the children to develop skills and understandings and express their ideas in an informal learning situation in which they do not have to worry about making mistakes, looking foolish or failing. Both free-play and directed play need to be planned if they are to provide the children with new experiences that will build on their previous learning and help them towards scientific ideas.

In our planning for informal learning some of the questions that we need to ask ourselves are:

- What skills, concepts or attitudes am I hoping the resource/activity will foster?
- How will they fit in with what the children already know? Will they provide learning opportunities for all or just some children?
- Is this likely to interest, stimulate and motivate the children?
- How are the children likely to respond? What difficulties are likely to arise? Am I able to deal with them if they do?
- How will I know if the children have learnt anything? Will I need to record it? If so, how?

By carefully planning the children's informal learning, we are valuing it. We are also in a stronger position when challenged by parents that "Sally hasn't done any proper work again today." Parents have a right to expect that their children are learning and if that can be shown to be happening in an informal as well as formal way, then parents are more likely to appreciate that "playing in the water" entails far more than is superficially implied. Although having a plan with clearly laid out objectives to show concerned parents at such times can be invaluable, the main reason for planning is to reflect on and try to provide for the needs of each child in our care.

The following example (figure 1.4) of a planning sheet for informal learning is taken from a teacher's file. It outlines the learning anticipated for a group of children by asking a classroom auxiliary (Mrs G.) to initiate rule-bound play, in this case a game of 20

Questions using shells. This kind of record of classroom activity could be used, if necessary, to explain to interested parents that what might appear to be a simple game with shells that took half the morning was planned with particular learning in mind.

Date / time:

Group: *blue*   8.10.93. period ①

Activity: *sea-shells 20 questions*

Objectives: · sim. + diffs. btwn. shells
· observation / description
· question-raising
· deduction   · co-operation

Children's prior knowledge:
· shells found on sea shore
· animals live in them

Resources: shells
✻ Bring large conch from home. ✻

Teacher imput: Start off w shell all can see to
explain rules (Mrs. G.). Then on own.

Possible difficulties: formulating questions to yes/no ans.?
lang. to describe shells?

Learning outcomes: appreciate variety shells.
lang.

Record: Mrs. G. scribe questions for one shell
+ ans. Stick shell on. Use for display.

Other: if going O.K. cont. after break.

Figure 1.4 A teacher's plan for informal learning

Summary

Learning takes place in two main contexts – the formal and the informal. Both are equally important, as there is no one right way in which to learn; different ways will suit the differing needs of all children at different times. Children can be independent and self-directing learners from an early age and are capable of spending long hours absorbed in activities that they find of value and significance. We can capitalise on this in school by providing them with some time in which to follow their own interests rather than only those that we think appropriate. Children learn best when they are motivated and interested in what they are doing, are stimulated by it and themselves feel a need for it. A young child who wants to know what makes the hands go round on a clock may informally learn a great deal about energy transfer by taking an old clock to pieces. Informal learning is as essential as formal learning and needs to be valued as such, and not considered an alternative to 'work' to be done once 'work' is finished. This requires careful planning of activities, time and resources.

2 The formal learning of science

The reason why we need good science teaching – and we do need it, most urgently – has nothing to do with content, facts and practicalities. The most pressing imperative is that we somehow reduce the gullibility among the population at large. That a large number of people accept, without question, any old codswallop that someone cares to tell them is one of the great social problems of our time.

Gerald Haigh, *Times Educational Supplement,* 1989

Learning science in school no longer means young children spending their primary years collecting and memorising isolated facts. To develop their understanding of science the children need to be involved in activities in which they are exploring, discovering, investigating and trying to make sense of the world around them. These doing, finding out and thinking activities form the core of primary school science. For young children such activities need to:

- be appropriate and relevant to the children and their world
- be structured and purposeful, so that the children can build on their understanding and progress at their own level
- be challenging, so that the children have something tangible to think about and have opportunities to make decisions for themselves
- encourage the children to transfer their skills and learning from one context to other contexts
- be carried out in a supportive and non-threatening atmosphere.

This kind of activity occurred when a group of eight year olds were investigating making shadows of different lengths using a torch and a cup. They already knew that a shadow would be made when the cup blocked the path of light. They discovered that they could make different lengths and shapes of horizontal shadows by keeping the cup in the same position but changing the height of the torch relative to it.

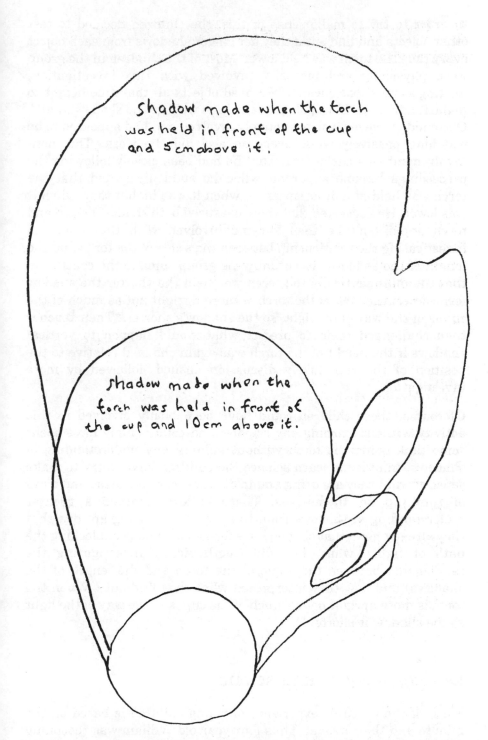

Shadow made when the torch
was held in front of the cup
and 5cm above it.

Shadow made when the
torch was held in front of
the cup and 10cm above it.

Figure 2.1 Trevor's drawing of the shadows formed by holding a torch at
two different heights in front of a cup

In order to try to make sense of this, the children decided to test other objects and find out if they got longer shadows from each object every time the torch was held lower. Most of the children in the group were physically and mentally involved with this investigation, making suggestions such as "We need objects all the same height to make it fair" and "If we hold it really high we'll get no shadow at all". One child, however, was not actively involved and had appeared to be watching passively while everyone else did the work. This non-involvement was misleading. That he had been closely following the proceedings became apparent, when he suddenly stated that the torch was held at a different angle when it was higher than when it was lower. He suggested that they measured both shadow length and torch angle, and he then became involved with the others in investigating the relationship between the angle of the torch and the length of the shadows. Eventually the group came to the conclusion that the more vertically the torch was held the shorter the shadow formed because "When the torch is more upright not as much of the cup is in the way of the light, so the shadow's shorter." Their teacher then challenged them to predict what would happen to vertical shadows if the height of the torch was again changed relative to the position of the cup. Lively discussion ensued, followed by more investigation.

Of course, these children could have been busily involved in this activity without learning any science, and could simply have spent some time using the torch without gaining any understanding of shadows. In order to learn science the children have to try to make sense of what they are doing and to develop scientific ideas and ways of thinking for themselves. These children gained a greater understanding of shadows from this activity by using an idea that they already held (that shadows are formed by an object blocking the path of light), what they did (methodically investigating the relationship between the angle of the torch and the length of the shadows) and how they interpreted what they find out ("When the torch is more upright not as much of the cup is in the way of the light so the shadow is shorter.").

Devices for learning science

Much of the scientific experience of young children is based on the minute and the personal. Thus four year old William was reasoning from a human-centred point of view when he looked at an autumn tree and asked, "How does the tree tell the leaf it's its turn to fall off next?"

In order to help the children progress from the personal to the abstract and to become conscious learners, we may have to teach them specific learning devices. A learning device is simply an approach that a learner can employ to enable him to learn something more easily. Obviously, to be able to use such a device requires that the learner knows about it. To have a range of devices available is even more advantageous, as it allows the learner to select and use the one or more that is appropriate to the learning in hand. Different kinds of learning in science require different devices.

kind of learning	learning device which could be used	example
remembering	*mnemonics*	*ROY G BIV for remembering sequence of colours of the rainbow*
hypothesising	*drawing on previous knowledge*	*suggesting that road condition may affect vehicle stopping distances e.g. "It takes longer to stop my bike if the road's wet."*
predicting	*putting information in such a way that can be tested*	*"I think the wadding will insulate better than the wool because it's thicker."*
developing new skills	*attempting a new activity*	*recording data in a variety of different ways*
demonstrating competency	*practising*	*reading a thermometer accurately*
explaining	*discussing*	*asserting that their conclusions are valid as they controlled relevant variables in a fair test*
insight	*reflecting*	*realising that Granddad's torch won't work because the circuit is broken*

Figure 2.2   Some examples of different kinds of learning and devices which learners could use in science sessions

We may have to use some science sessions especially to teach the children a learning device. So planning or thinking about the possible approaches to an investigation could become the focus of a science session rather than the investigation itself, in order that the children learn about ways to plan. Copying or making lists in order to help remember something is a device many older learners use, but is one that may need teaching to young children. Similarly, imitating is a device we all use; but some children may need to be reassured that it is all right to do so, and that it is not cheating. The children may need to be reminded from time to time that they have a particular device available to them. They may also have learnt some devices in other subject areas and yet may not realise that the same devices can be used in science. So we may have to show the children where the science books are in the library and how they can access them, or remind them to use an index to look up the life-cycle of the butterfly.

Roles and learning

The extent to which children employ learning devices, and the devices that they choose, depends not only on their knowledge of available devices but also on the role that they adopt at the time. A role is a mode in which children operate at any given time. It is not a personality type. However, children can sometimes get so stuck in a particular role that it becomes a part of their character. The child who adopts a clowning role time after time may well become a jokey character. Roles are individually constructed and as such the children are in control of their roles and readily can, and do, switch roles. A clowning role can be dropped and a helpful one adopted, when a child wants to show off an encyclopaedia he has specially brought from home because "It's got photos of Titan and Mimas, two of Saturn's moons."

Children sometimes adopt a particular role with a particular subject. The adoption of a particular role is influenced as much by how easy or difficult they perceive the subject to be, as by their perception of their ability and their motivation to learn the subject. External forces such as how well they get on with the teacher, peer-group pressure, parental expectations and social attitudes also play a part. As teachers we need to be aware of the roles that the children adopt, as, once selected, a role can determine the learning devices that the children use, as well as their classroom behaviour and the kind and amount of learning that takes place. Some common roles which children may adopt include:

- *goody-goody* – follows worksheets implicitly, does exactly what teacher says/wants
- *brains* – asks questions no-one can answer, likes to know how and why things work
- *funny-kid* – mimics, clowns, jokes, uses scientific jargon in an attempt to impress
- *toughie* – creates diversions so that no-one realises he cannot do it or does not know
- *dilly-dreamer* – floats about doing as little as possible, suggests far-fetched solutions
- *nice-kid* – helps others, organises practical work, brings in books from home
- *flounderer* – copies, does what others do/say, avoids danger/problems/questions

Of course, children do not use either roles or learning devices solely in their learning of science or, indeed, only in formal education. When they consciously or unconsciously choose a role to adopt, the children are going through a decision-making process that may be neither rational nor logical. This decision will be based on various factors including:

i   their consideration of available possibilities. For example, when asked to fetch an unfamiliar piece of apparatus, the flounderer may try avoiding tactics by volunteering to take the register to the office in the hopes that somebody else will have been asked to fetch the apparatus by the time he gets back; or, conversely, may offer to fetch the apparatus ("Jo and I'll get it, Miss") and chooses someone who he thinks knows what is to be fetched.

ii their perception of the subject. "Electricity's hard." "Girls don't need to do electricity in real life. Dads always do it."

iii their attitude to it. "I hate doing electricity. I feel stupid because I can't understand it."

iv their personal relationships. "Will Jo help me today?" "What will Mr Green say when he finds out I can't do it?"

If the decision children make about a role is based on mistaken considerations it may result in the adoption of an inappropriate role. This can affect not only their classroom behaviour but the learning devices that they use and the learning that takes place. From this perspective it can be seen that learning can be quite haphazard. However, if we are able to raise the children's awareness of both roles and learning devices we can help them to realise that they also have some degree of responsibility for their own learning and development. Simply reflecting the children's comments back to them is a way of raising their awareness:

i   "Do you and Jo both know what to look for?"

ii "Is it really true that girls don't need to do electricity? How would you manage if your Dad was away?"

iii "Let's find out what you already understand about electricity. I bet it's more than you think."

iv "Have a go at that circuit diagram on your own. If you get stuck, fetch all the bits you think we'll need and we'll look at it together."

Formal school science

Formal learning in school is different in many ways from the informal learning that takes place in and out of school. Formal learning is deliberate in its requirement that the children learn particular kinds of things in particular ways at particular times, in order to become proficient in specific skills and subjects. In science, as in other curricular areas, young children often have very little choice about what they are expected to learn and how and when they are expected to learn it. Such limitations tend to occur when the learning of science is mistakenly equated with the learning of scientific facts. However, the learning of science is much more than the learning of facts. Primary science aims to help the children to find out about both natural and made world and to attempt to make sense of them through:

* learning to ask questions and finding ways of answering them satisfactorily
* understanding the key concepts of science
* using scientific methods of investigation
* appreciating the provisional nature of scientific knowledge and explanation.

If we consider science as a way of seeing, doing and thinking rather than a subject to be learned, we need to encourage the children to make sense of what they are doing and to develop scientific ideas and ways of thinking for themselves. We can help them to do this by gradually developing their:

- use of a range of skills. Being able to reflect, select, enquire, explain and so on helps the children with decision making and problem solving.
- knowledge of the biological and physical world. Knowing more about the world around them and the way in which it affects them allows the children to make more informed choices and can contribute to their safety and health.
- appreciation of attitudes. Young children can be encouraged to persevere, be honest, sensitive and so on and to take responsibility for their thoughts and actions.

In primary science these three attributes of skills, knowledge and attitudes are so closely intertwined and supportive of each other that they cannot easily be taught or learnt separately. For example, six year old Maisie was selecting and testing fabrics in order to find one that was suitable for use as a parachute. In order to do this she had to draw on the ideas that she already held about of the concept of gravity; plan what she wanted to do; use her skills of measuring both fabric size and time; co-operate with her friends for the use of the stop clock; raise questions and try to find answers to them; then to reflect on what she had done and found out in order to explain why she considered a particular fabric the most suitable.

For good science to take place, the children need to use their skills in an atmosphere that encourages positive attitudes so that they can develop their understanding of scientific concepts. As in all areas of their development, the children have to start from where they are at any given moment and build on their previous learning in order to make progress. As a result they may start from different points in their learning of scientific skills, concepts and attitudes and may not progress at the same rate in each.

Skills

Children develop their scientific skills as they process information about the objects and phenomena that they experience. When monitoring plant growth a group of eight year old children developed skills of observing, describing, questioning, measuring, evaluating and reflecting while they drew on, considered and modified the ideas that they held about plants as living organisms. With practice and experience the children's skills develop from partly formed, commonplace ones to ones that are more refined and scientific. So they are able to progress from making simple suggestions such as,

"Plants will grow taller if they are given plant food than if they are not", to discerning predictions, such as "The variable composition of different types of compost may be a factor that affects the height of a plant from the time a seed is sown."

Research[1] has shown that primary teachers seem to be over-optimistic in believing that the science activities young children undertake allow them to practise a wide range of skills. Many of the activities we provide invariably use observation and communication and neglect other skills. We need to be aware of the functions of practical activities so that the children have different kinds of experiences in order to develop their:

a physical skills

Two eight year olds, John and Adam, who needed practice in reading a thermometer, were provided with an opportunity to find out which material would be the best for a tea cosy. John wrote:

We put hot water in four metal tea pots and wrapped one in wool material and one in felt and one in aluminium foil and left one with nothing on.

Water temperature after 10 minutes:

Wool material 40°C   Felt 37°C   Foil 34°C   Nothing 30°C

Water temperature after 20 minutes:

Wool material 35°C   Felt 31°C   Foil 26°C   Nothing 21°C

The wool material kept the water warmest so we think that's the best.

b mental skills

Considering the disappearance of water from a saucer placed in the sun encouraged six year old Mark to develop a mental model to help with his understanding of evaporation.

Today we put some water into a saucer and put it on the windowsill. I think the sun is drying up the water and tomorrow all the water will be gone because the sun just dries it up.

Mark

c social skills

As part of a topic on movement, a teacher gave her class of nine year olds a challenge "to make something that'll move 1 metre". When commenting on this activity afterwards the teacher said:

Before the children started I gave them time to discuss and plan and encouraged them to think about different sources of energy. They shared their ideas and plans and experimented with materials then used a variety of ways of making their things move, such as twisted and stretched rubber bands, air pressure, gravity and magnets. They worked well together but needed to be encouraged to overcome some of the problems they encountered and helped to deal with their failures, but they persevered.

d mathematical skills

Seven year old Samantha was encouraged to develop her mathematical skills by measuring the growth of a sunflower seedling. Initially she chose to note the measurements as a list in her book:

Monday	*0 cm.*
Tuesday	*1 cm.*
Wednesday	*3 cm.*
Thursday	*4 cm.*
Friday	*5 cm.*
Monday	*8 cm.*
Tuesday	*10 cm.*
Wednesday	*11 cm.*
Thursday	*11 cm.*
Friday	*14 cm.*

She then realised that a list was probably not the best way to record the growth and so she changed method and displayed her results as a graph (figure 2.3).

e linguistic skills

Discussing the results of a investigation into the acidity of rain provided four 10 year olds with opportunities to develop their linguistic skills. As Allen explained to the rest of the class:

We collected rain from January to March. In that time the pH of the rain varied between 5.8 and 4.0. The rain wasn't the same every day because the wind was blowing from different directions and bringing different levels of pollution in the air. The most acidic rain that fell had a pH of 4.0. This is quite worrying because we found out that below pH 4.8 damage to the environment can be quite serious.

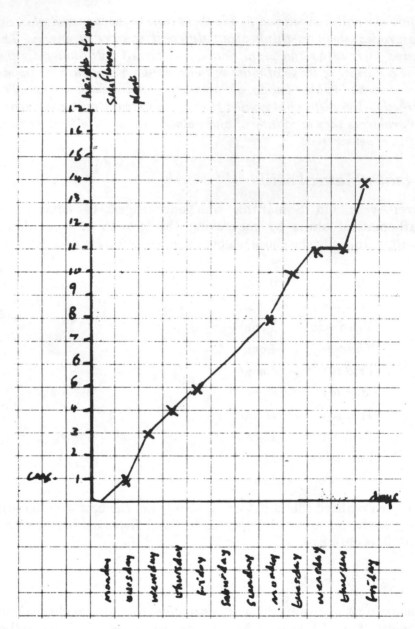

Figure 2.3   Samantha's graph of the daily growth of her sunflower
seedling

Many of the activities we ask young children to carry out use their
skills of observation. However, when a number of children are
observing the same object or action, there will be diversity in the
observations they make, as they see different things as important,
give different reasons for what they see, draw different conclusions
or have different ideas because they are influenced by their previous

experiences and background. These three descriptions were made five year olds after careful observation of the same hamster:

We looked at the hamster and it is light brown and a bit of dark brown.   Justin

It's a she and she's got red eyes and all the time she sniffs because hamsters can't see very well so she sniffs to see what's going on.
                                                                          Azeem

Her face is brown and under her chin is white and her nose shines and she has big pouches in her cheeks. She is a sweet thing and I hope she'll live for a long time.   Natalie

The children can be encouraged to observe more carefully by, for example, making notes or completing a chart that draws their attention to the appearance of an object – its size, shape, colour, texture and so on, or by using all their senses, or appropriate measuring tools or a hand lens or microscope. Young children often need encouragement to describe what they actually see and not what they think they see. Even when they have based their ideas on what they have observed, their inability to abstract and generalise can occasionally cause them to use contradictory ideas to explain something. They are often either unaware of any conflict or capable of ignoring it, and not only insist on clinging to their different ideas but can easily switch from one idea to another. Five year old Sean had been observing a snail moving and was talking about his understanding of 'alive' with his teacher:

Sean: *Alive things move.*

Teacher: *So is this snail alive?*

Sean: [laughing] *No, course not.*

Teacher: *Why not? It's moving.*

Sean: *Yeah, but it's only a snail. Snails in't alive. They're not real.*

Teacher: *Not real?*

Sean: *No. It's like... It's not alive.*

Teacher: *So it's moving but it's not alive?*

Sean: *Yeah.*

Teacher: *So what is alive? Tell me some things that are alive.*

Sean: *Dogs 'n' cats. You know, animals.*

Sean's idea of alive is narrower than a biological one, in which living organisms, both plants and animals, are distinguished from dead ones by being able to move, feed, grow, breathe, excrete, reproduce and use their senses. Sean initially states that alive things move. He goes on to say that animals are alive. Sean appears to mean that mammals are the only animals that are alive and can move, although he agrees that the snail is moving. He is able to hold these conflicting ideas because he does not consider the snail to be 'real'. Sean's teacher then asked him why he thought cats and dogs were alive and if he could tell her what sort of things he thought they could do. She then asked him if he could think of any other animals that could also move, eat and so on. He only mentioned mammals and so she drew his attention back to the snail and asked if that could eat as well as move. Sean had no idea but enthusiastically decided to put the snail in with some leaves and watch it to find out. His enthusiasm waned, however, and the snail escaped, never to be found. When a few days later he found a hole in the page of a library book he showed it to his teacher with the comment "I bet that snail ate that."

Providing an audience can be an effective way of giving the children a purpose for looking accurately and then *describing* their observations. Five year old Katie had observed a slug and then described it to a group of children by saying:

It's brown and all shiny. It made this silver line like a snail. It's like a snail. It's a snail what's parked its shell.

As Katie had already chosen to compare the slug to a snail, her teacher encouraged her to look further at the similarities and differences between slugs and snails in order to develop her skill of *classifying*. As the two animals are both gastropods and in fact quite similar, she suggested that Katie made a list of the similarities and differences between the two in order to help her to focus on precise features (figure 2.4).

Being able to identify and classify involves the children in noticing patterns or relationships between things, and makes them look for differences of detail in order to distinguish relevant aspects from those that are not so important. After Katie had made her list, she joined a group of children who were using a binary key to sort a

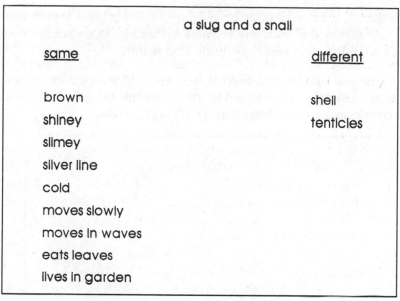

a slug and a snail

same	different
brown	shell
shiney	tenticles
slimey	
silver line	
cold	
moves slowly	
moves in waves	
eats leaves	
lives in garden	

Figure 2.4   Katie's list of the similarities between a slug and a snail

collection of different mini beasts. The children initially sorted the collection into two distinct groups by asking of each mini beast:

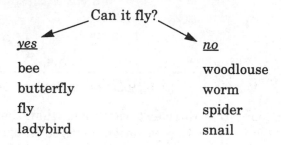

Can it fly?

yes	no
bee	woodlouse
butterfly	worm
fly	spider
ladybird	snail

They then asked:

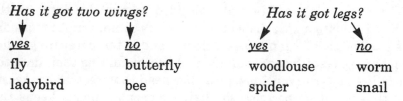

Has it got two wings?		Has it got legs?	
yes	no	yes	no
fly	butterfly	woodlouse	worm
ladybird	bee	spider	snail

They continued to ask questions until the groups could not be further sub-divided. Katie then worked through the questions and by answering each one was able to identify the group to which her slug belonged.

Searching for patterns in data is another scientific skill that children can be encouraged to develop. In order to do this they need to be able to obtain or retrieve information from different sources, as well as generating their own data by investigations. They need opportunities to store information, both written and numerical, in a variety of ways and to be able to interpret, evaluate and use it.

Nine year olds Herb and Shakti had been learning how to use a liquid crystal strip thermometer by investigating the variation in skin temperature on different parts of their bodies.

	Shakti	Herb
head	33°	35°
tummy	32°	34°
knee	31°	32°
foot	30°	29°

Figure 2.5   Variations of skin temperature in degrees Centigrade

Both of them found that their feet were cooler than their heads and wondered if this temperature variation occurred in everyone. Their teacher encouraged them to find out and so they decided to take the temperatures of the different parts of the body of every other member of the class. They also decided to put the data, as they collected it, onto a spreadsheet on the class computer. As more data was entered they began to see a clear trend of temperature gradient from head to feet for each individual. After examining their data they concluded that everyone has a warmer head than feet and suggested that this might be because the hair on people's heads keeps their heads warmer. From this they hypothesised that completely bald people's heads should not be that much warmer than their feet. Unfortunately they were unable to test this hypothesis properly due to a lack of suitably bald people!

Many of the scientific skills that young children are expected to develop pertain to *investigation*. At a simple level an investigation requires the children to systematically generate data that they can then use to support or challenge explanations of why objects or events are as they are. Thus there is always a thinking aspect to an investigation; it is not simply following instructions and handling equipment. An investigation differs from an experiment or test in that it always includes some kind of evaluation of the reliability of the data collected and the validity of the conclusions drawn. A group of nine year olds who had investigated (rather than experimented or tested) how the solubility of salt and sugar was affected by the temperature of water, afterwards realised that their investigation would have been more reliable and repeatable if they had measured the amount of salt and sugar that they had used in grams rather than teaspoons because "When we measured the salt and sugar with the teaspoon, sometimes we could have put a bit more on the spoon than other times". This evaluation of their methodology caused them to decide that the data they had collected was not accurate enough for them to be certain that the conclusions that they had drawn were valid.

As they develop their investigative skills, young children can increasingly take responsibility for planning and carrying out a series of actions, the key features of which are:

- *stating* clearly what they are investigating
- *planning* what to do before starting, including considering the equipment, time and space that will be needed, any potential problems and safety aspects
- *having an idea* about what they are going to change systematically during the investigation – 'the independent variable'
- *deciding* what and how they are going to measure – the 'dependent variable'
- *thinking* about what they are going to keep the same in order to make it a fair test – the 'control variables'
- *choosing* an appropriate way in which to record/present their data
- *checking* that their data and conclusions apply to what they have investigated and that they are realistic and believable.

Investigations sometimes arise as a result of the children *hypothesising*. A hypothesis is based on the children using their existing knowledge and observations to think and raise questions about certain objects, events or situations. By *predicting* what they think might happen and then investigating it, children can test their hypothesis scientifically. Two seven year old boys had exasperated their teacher by persistently twanging a ruler off the edge of a desk, so she decided to capitalise on the knowledge that they had gained about the relationship between the length of the ruler and the note produced, by challenging them to design a musical instrument that worked on the same principle. The teacher encouraged them first to use their existing knowledge to hypothesise about the relationship between length and pitch. They predicted that they would get a higher note by plucking a short, taut string than a long one. They systematically investigated this in order to test their hypothesis and then evaluated their results and conclusions. Afterwards they discussed this activity with each other and the teacher, and were able to use their ideas to help them design a simple musical instrument that had fishing line of different lengths stretched tightly between nails on a triangular wooden frame:

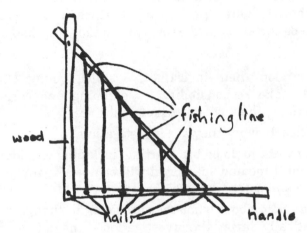

Figure 2.6   A design for a musical instrument by two seven year old boys

Evaluation of what has been done is an important part of an investigation and consists of two distinct entities: checking for validity and checking for reliability. Young children can be encouraged to consider the *validity* of their investigation by looking at what they have done and checking that their conclusions apply to what they have investigated. For example, a group of nine year olds had investigated how the stopping distances of bicycles are affected by the conditions of the road. Afterwards they checked that they had tried a variety of road conditions (wet, dry, muddy, gravely); that they had measured the stopping distances; that they had ensured it was a 'fair test' by controlling variables such as the bicycles used, how fast the bicycles were going before the brakes were applied, how hard the brakes were applied and so on. They were therefore quite sure that their investigation had been a valid one and that the conclusions that they had drawn about the stopping distances and the road conditions were indeed substantive. In order to check the *reliability* of their results they considered whether their data and their answers were believable by asking themselves questions such as: Was the design of our investigation suitable? Did we actually investigate what we set out to investigate? Did we choose a realistic way of taking and recording our measurements? Were our measurements accurate? Were they repeatable?

Communicating the results of an investigation involves the children in letting others know what they did and what they found out and is a skill that can enhance understanding for both the children and the teacher. The children's use of language to inform or instruct is not the same as their everyday talk because it requires them to be more precise than they may usually be, and to some extent this can make it artificial.

Communication can be verbal or non-verbal and may include the use of symbols, models, diagrams, graphs, tables, charts and so on. The children need to experience a variety of means of communicating and a variety of types of audience in order to learn how to choose an appropriate method of presentation. Communicating also involves the children in receiving information from others at first hand or from secondary sources such as books, pictures and television, and being able to understand it and respond to it.

When communicating what they have done or seen, young children often do not distinguish between a description of a phenomenon and an explanation for a phenomenon and we may have to urge them to go beyond simply using their senses in order to consider what has caused the effect that they are telling us about. When asked why something has happened, they will often say what has happened. They are frequently content to accept that what has happened has happened and do not require a reason or explanation for it. Seven year old Alex was asked to draw a picture to show how she could hear her teacher telling the class to be quiet. Her picture only showed what had happened and when asked about it Alex simply said, "Mr Barnes tells us to be quiet" and did not attempt an explanation.

Mr Barnes looked at her picture and then asked her: *So did you hear me go "Shhhs"?*

Alex: *Yes.*

Mr Barnes: *How did you hear me go "Shhhs"?*

Alex: *With my ears.*

Mr Barnes: *So how did the "Shhhs" go from my mouth to your ear?*

Figure 2.7   Alex's 'explanation' of how she could hear Mr Barnes telling the class to be quiet

Alex: *Like this.* (Alex puts her hand by Mr Barnes' mouth and moves it in a straight line to her right ear.)

Mr Barnes: *So the "Shhhs" go straight from my mouth to this ear. What about the other ear? Did that hear the "Shhhs" too?*

Alex: Yea.   *They went to that ear too. Half went to that ear* (points to right ear) *and half went to that ear* (points to left ear).

Mr Barnes: *Can you draw how it goes on your picture?*

This line of questioning encouraged Alex to attempt a simple explanation of how she thought she could hear Mr Barnes telling the class to keep quiet. As the children's scientific knowledge and understanding develop they also become more able to use science to explain why things are as they are. The use of key sentences, such as 'What we did' and 'What we found out' can help the children to appreciate the difference between *describing* what they have done and *explaining* what happened and why it happened. A group of ten year olds investigated sound vibrations and afterwards wrote:

What did we do? *We hit the tuning fork against a chair leg and then put it up to somebody's ear. When the person could not hear the sounds, the person stopped the stopwatch. Then we did the same thing, but we dipped the end of the tuning fork in water and then put it up to somebody's ear. When the person could not hear the sounds, the person stopped the stopwatch.*

What did we find out? *We found out that when we dipped the end of the tuning fork in water the sound did not last as long as the sound out of the water because the water stopped some of the vibrations.*

As their skills grow, we may need to help the children to realise that they have acquired skills that are relevant, and that those skills are not just for school use but are ones that they can use in their daily lives. For example, we can help the children to appreciate that their planning skills are ones that they can also apply to tackling problems such as making a bird box for Grandma's birthday present, as they would need to think about the design, materials, where it is to be positioned, the kind of bird that is to use it and so on, before fetching equipment and starting to make it. Informed judgement is a skill that the children can put to use when choosing a snack, if they are encouraged to make a decision based on their knowledge of health and nutrition. Similarly, the careful and considered use of equipment is a skill that the children can utilise in cooking, if they are given the opportunity to choose for themselves the implements to use and allowed to measure out their ingredients. Drawing conclusions and reflecting on the validity of those conclusions are skills that can help to inform the children's decision making, if they are allowed to choose and wear the clothes that they think are appropriate for the weather when playing outside. Presenting conclusions and information are skills that older children can use in putting forward a case or a side in an argument, such as when trying to persuade Mum to buy recycled toilet paper.

Concepts

Concepts can be thought of as ideas or general notions of the attributes that are common to a class of objects or events. So the concept of 'cat' would encompass all the essential qualities that are the same for all cats – facial whiskers, retractable claws, meat eater and so on, and would apply as equally to the big cats (lions, tigers, etc.) as to domestic ones. The concept of cat can be sub-divided into smaller concepts that enable us to distinguish a puma from a stray tabby or a champion Persian blue. The more concepts are subdivided into smaller and smaller sub-concepts the more specific and restrictive they become. Conversely the larger the concept, the more wide-ranging and abstract it is. Thus 'cat' is a subset of the concept 'carnivore', which in turn is a subset of the concept 'mammal'.

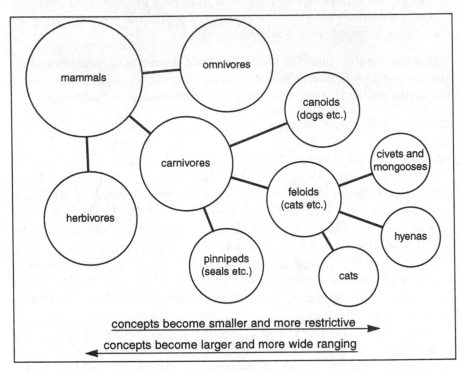

Figure 2.8   Concepts can be sub-divided into smaller and smaller sub-concepts

Similarly, science concepts can be thought of as those ideas or general notions of the common attributes of objects or events that help us to understand order in the natural and physical world around us. They enable us to appreciate the patterns and relationships between the way things are made and the way they behave, whether it is the structure and function of a leaf, why a rainbow appears as it does or the manufacture of the latest space shuttle. In the primary school, science is often grouped into three broad concepts that relate to:

- the characteristics and classification of living and non-living things
- how living and non-living things behave, work and interact with each other
- how living and non-living things can change state, form or position.

The National Curriculum and many primary science texts delineate the smaller concepts that make up these larger concepts. The larger science concepts are more wide ranging and abstract, whereas smaller ones more restrictive and specific. Thus, 'sound' is a large and abstract concept for most young children, whereas the noise made by banging a drum is a smaller and more accessible concept for them. In our teaching it is often easiest for children if we provide them with opportunities to move from the smaller science concepts with which they are likely to be more familiar to broader, general and more abstract ones. We can do this by:

- helping the children to link their existing ideas to a new object or event so that they can use them to make sense of the new situation ("You said that a longer string makes a lower note because there's more of it to vibrate. So why do you think you get a lower note when you cover more holes of your recorder?")

- encouraging the children to interact with other people's ideas in order to increase the range of ideas and understandings available to them ("Well, as Mrs Briggs is conducting, why don't you ask her what difference it makes to the overall sound to put the violins on both sides, or see if you can find a library book that explains about the layout of an orchestra?")

- encouraging the children to articulate and refine their ideas by trying to explain them to others ("Mohammed, tell us why you think the noise is different when we hit different chime bars.")

In order to learn about a new concept with understanding, the children have to broaden their ideas for themselves so that the new makes sense of in terms of what they already know. Of course, the children can learn a new concept by rote, but invariably rote learning does not link with existing knowledge and so is not likely to have been understood. Although a group of postgraduate trainee teachers studying forces were all able to remember learning at school that "Force equals mass times acceleration ($F = m$ x a)", very few of them had any idea of its meaning or its relevance and as a result were unable to make use of it even in a physics lesson. These teachers had to put their rote learning to one side and consider what they already knew about forces. By starting from their existing ideas they were then able to broaden their understanding of forces.

It takes time for concepts to develop; and so they are unlikely to be learnt with understanding if only encountered once in one particular context. New concepts are more likely to link with existing ideas and make sense if they are developed through a variety of different contexts and activities. A teacher of nine year olds who wanted to develop the concept of light travelling in straight lines, used work with shadows, beams of light, toilet roll tubes and periscopes, so that by testing their ideas in different contexts the children had more opportunities to link this new concept with their existing knowledge. However, an activity may develop more than one concept at any one time. So, as well as developing the concept that light travels in straight lines, these children also developed ideas about how light is reflected and that shadows are formed by blocking the path of light.

There is no one 'right' way to teach any specific concept. Some ways will be more relevant or reliable, more appropriate or easier to carry out for some concepts than others. Whatever way is used, a range of contexts needs to be found that is suitable for both children and teachers. The freedom to choose the different contexts through which to teach a concept allows teachers to take advantage of their own strengths, the children's interests and the resources available. As the National Curriculum does not specify the contexts by which science concepts should be taught, teachers are still able to choose how they will teach them.

For a long time topic teaching in the primary school has enabled work in one subject area to enhance and reinforce the learning in another so that the learning process is a coherent one. As the National Curriculum has been presented from a discrete disciplinary perspective, some schools have chosen to teach some aspects of science within clearly science-focused topics. Whether science is taught as part of a topic or as a specific subject is, in the end, a school decision. However, The Association for Science Education advises primary schools that:

> The most important aspect of effective science teaching is the relevance of the contextual framework in which it is placed, rather than whether it is approached through a topic or a subject specific method. We would advocate a balance of approaches used at different times, leaving teachers to use the approach which is most suited to their purpose.[2]

Attitudes

Science in primary schools is invariably taught not only by non-specialist teachers, but often by teachers whose own experience of school science was brief, alienating and none too happy; and who may have had very little scientific training and lack both confidence and competence in science. However, apart from their own scientific education, teachers will have acquired ideas about science as a result of socialisation; and such ideas, either consciously or unconsciously, will permeate their teaching. Although science is generally considered an objective and disinterested discipline, in practice it is not value free as it has social as well as political, economic and moral aspects. *In vitro* fertilisation, for example, is a contentious area. Both its practice and research are dependent on advances in science and technology, and require financial and political support. Yet most of us have (possibly strong) ideas about its value, the social and moral implications of supporting the production of children in this way, and the ethics of genetic engineering.

Teachers' views about the social, political, economic and moral aspects of science may well influence both their practice and any strategies, such as selection of resources or mode of presentation, that they adopt. Young children too will have views about some of the social, political, economic and moral aspects of science. Although they may have only a limited or even a distorted knowledge of science or scientific issues, they can get quite emotional about topics such as drugs, global warming or third world issues. By helping the children to realise that science is a way of 'viewing the world' rather than 'a truth', we can encourage an accepting classroom atmosphere in which they can reflect on alternatives, learn how to choose between them and in which they can be open rather than 'right'. This may mean that we have to try not to let our own views of a subject unduly influence the children and instead provide them with opportunities to make up their own minds and form their own opinions. For example, when discussing smoking we can present the facts and support those facts with evidence and give the children a chance to express their own views and to consider both the facts and other people's opinions about it, rather than attempt to influence the children with our own (possibly strong) views on the subject. Similarly we need to be careful not to evaluate from our own point of view and as a result approve or disapprove of the children's ideas and values. If the children feel that their subjective values are 'wrong', they may also conclude that any decision based on those values is also 'wrong'.

Attitudes to science also have an indirect effect on children's learning. All teachers convey attitudes either consciously or unconsciously. Thus a teacher's body language on confronting a grass snake that a child has brought to show her can give a far more powerful message about her attitude towards snakes than her weak "Very interesting, dear. Why don't you show Mrs Richardson? She likes that sort of thing." By being aware of our attitudes in relation to science, we can become more open about different perspectives.

"I'm sorry, I really do not like snakes. Put it over there and then tell me why you find it so interesting."

The children's attitudes to life and to each other are influenced by the atmosphere in which they work and the people with whom they work. These attitudes are acquired rather than learned and often are unconsciously developed by example: not only the example set by the teacher, but by the classroom atmosphere. The books, posters, videos, and objects in the classroom can inadvertently reflect either positive or negative images of science. Whilst choice of resources may be limited by availability, we need to consider whether they:

- dispel the stereotypical views that science is a fundamentally male, remote, abstract and Western activity (flick through any textbook or video and note whether illustrations depict only white males involved in science activities)

- illustrate the cultural diversity of science and its relevance to different cultures (are there examples from different parts of the world? Are those examples ones that are make sense to the children in your class?)

- develop images of science that highlight variety in the methods and approaches used (many children, and adults, still have an image of science that involves only test tubes and bunsen-burners)

- demonstrate that scientific ideas and methods have evolved throughout history and are not a recent invention (information about scientists in the past and the great discoveries brings science to life).

Children's attitudes to science will also be determined to some extent by the roles that they adopt and the learning devices that they employ. These will affect their willingness to take part in activities and the ways in which they respond to people, objects and situations. The children gain in self-discipline, perseverance, originality and other important attitudes not so much by what the teacher says or does, but by the way in which it is said or done, by the encouragement that they are offered, and from the learning situation that is created.

The attitudes that children have toward science will also influence their learning – whether they are comfortable with doing science, suspicious or scared of the equipment, trust the scientific evidence and so on. We can engender positive attitudes towards science by encouraging the children to:

- be curious about new or unusual scientific objects or events
- look at objects or events in detail

- ask questions and offer opinions
- tolerate uncertainty and accept that science can not always provide the answers to questions
- respect the opinions of others and accept critical reflection
- evaluate their own work or ideas in order to improve them.

Parental expectations and pressures will also influence the children's attitudes to science. Parents will have their own views of the social, political, economic and moral aspects of science and scientific issues; and if science is valued in the home, the children are far more likely to acquire positive attitudes towards it. Parents' understanding of the science that their children do in primary school often appears to be based on their ideas of what science is and their own experiences of science at secondary school level. We can raise parents' awareness of the scientific experiences that their children are having and the learning opportunities with which they are provided, by encouraging parental involvement in science fairs and practical workshops.

Summary

Science is taught to young children in order to help them develop disciplined ways of thinking about objects and phenomena. By using their scientific skills and developing their understanding of more abstract and wide ranging ideas, they are in a better position to try and make sense of the world about them. We can help the children to examine their ideas, question their thoughts and to accept that all our scientific understandings are necessarily only partial and of a tentative nature. In order to be good learners of science, the children need a supportive and non-threatening learning environment both at home and at school, as well as positive attitudes and a willingness to learn. The kind and amount of learning that takes place will be determined to some extent by their classroom behaviour, the learning devices that they use and the roles that they adopt, so the children will need to be encouraged to realise that they also have some responsibility for their own learning.

References

1 Newton D, 'Children Doing Science' in Newton L (ed.), *Primary science: the challenge of the 1990s*, Multilingual Matters Ltd, Clevedon, 1992, p 17

2 ASE, *The whole curriculum in primary schools: maintaining quality in the teaching of primary science,* The Association for Science Education, Hatfield, 1993, para 4.3

3 The child as a learner of science

... errors in children's thinking should be treated as informative rather than merely incorrect.

Richard T White, *Learning Science*

Children's everyday experiences, in and out of school, enable them to gain ideas and to make interpretations and explanations about what they do and see and feel. A group of five year olds was asked by their teacher to write down any ideas that they had about energy. One girl wrote:

Wires have energy for the lights. A traffic light has energy for cars. A car has energy for to help it go. A cooker has energy. Energy is a kind of electricity that is used in houses and factories to make the machines work to make cars and other things like chairs.

A boy wrote:

People running is energy and the cars can be energy and watches can be energy. Many things can be energy and the people doing things can use energy.

Of course, any views that children express in their writing may be constrained by factors such as their physical ability to write and the time available in which to do so. Here, both children recognise that a range of different things use energy and that energy enables something to happen. The girl expresses a narrower view of energy than the boy, as she restricts herself to ideas about electrical energy, whereas the boy also notes a biological type of energy. However, the girl is aware of factories and machines and realises that they use energy. These two children have constructed different and very personal ideas about energy because of the influence of their different life experiences. These children were able to explore their ideas further through discussion and were then provided with an opportunity to extended their ideas when their teacher challenged them to think of, and find out about, other types of energy.

Even when the children have had similar experiences of energy, they may not necessarily interpret them in the same way or remember the same details, as each is influenced by his own personal experiences and interpretations. A trip down the nearest street with a group of five year olds to "find out how many different things we can see which use energy", will produce diverse opinions as each child sees and interprets differently. Such an outing helps each child to re-experience energy, as it provides an opportunity for him to hear ideas put forward by others. He will need time after his experience in which to reflect on the ideas he has heard and to consider them in the light of the ideas that he already holds. New ideas need to be used and tested in a variety of situations in order to be reviewed, accepted and consolidated; and this can only happen over a period of time.

Children are sometimes unwilling to change their existing ideas. This is a particular difficulty when they hold ideas that are scientifically incorrect and yet insist on clinging to them. Attempts by teachers and parents will not necessarily persuade them to change, as even when the children are given evidence to show that their ideas are wrong, they are quite capable of ignoring it or interpreting it in terms of the ideas they already hold. This is because understanding is a process by which children test and modify their ideas. However, if their ideas are not in a form that is testable, no amount of evidence will help them to modify them.

Lynsey, age six, held an extremely stable idea about the digestive system, which her teacher could not persuade her to change.

First we chew the food up. Then there are two tubes, one for food and one for drink. Then some muscles mush it together. Then it comes out of one end.

Lynsey knew from her own experience that solid and liquid foods go separately into the body. She also knew that solids and liquids are eliminated separately from the body. She thus concluded that they must pass through the body separately, and so the idea of two distinct tubes made complete sense to her. Lynsey was not prepared to change her idea at that particular time, despite being shown pictures of the digestive system. She was adamant that her digestive system was not the same as those in the pictures.

At the end of a period of teaching we may discover that some children have not changed their ideas at all, or made the links for which we hoped for. Instead of blaming ourselves for failing those children, as we sometimes do, or blaming the children themselves, perhaps we should be asking ourselves whether the children are holding ideas that are in a testable form. Have we perhaps made assumptions that because they are of a particular age, the children have already constructed certain basic scientific ideas? Have we given the children formalised scientific knowledge that they cannot link to their existing ideas?

In any group of children there is likely to be a range of ideas held about a given subject. For example, a class of five year olds had watched a television programme about floating and sinking. Afterwards they were asked why they thought the turnip had floated.

Vanessa: *The turnip floated because it was old.*

Jenny: *The turnip floated because it was small.*

Michael: *It stayed above the water because it had no holes in it. If it had holes it would sink.*

These children's ideas do not accord with scientific explanations about floating. However, rather than point out to the children that their ideas are wrong, their teacher encouraged them to explore the implications of their ideas and to investigate their assertions. "Does that mean that all old things float then?" she asked Vanessa. Vanessa was not sure but thought she could find some old things to test so that she could try to find out. Similarly, Jenny and Michael were encouraged to test small and holey things. By taking their ideas seriously and encouraging them to test them, their teacher gave the children opportunities to re-think and modify them. They found out that not all old, small and things without holes float, although some do, and instead decided that perhaps the turnip had floated "because it wasn't heavy." This, of course, led to a further round of testing!

Children sometimes hold ideas that are narrower and more limited than those we hold as adults. For example, young children sometimes explain that the different phases of the moon occur "Because the clouds are in front of it". If they cannot see a full moon it must be because something is in the way. Sometimes they use quite contradictory reasonings to explain a phenomenon and easily change from one explanation to another. Often such ideas are context-dependent as children tend to see different situations as instances of different phenomena, even when the underlying phenomenon may be the same. Depending on the context they may switch from one explanation to another contradictory one, with no apparent awareness of any conflict, because their experiences to date have led them to believe that is how things work in practice. Thus nine year old Joy drew two completely contradictory ideas about how she was able to see a candle and a cup.

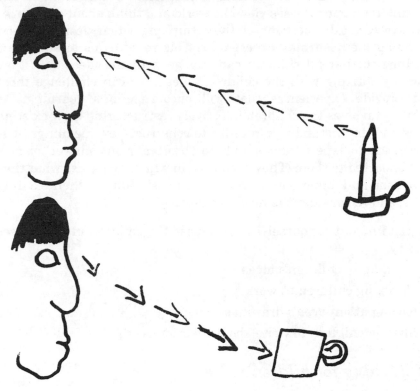

Figure 3.1   A nine year old's drawing of how she was able to see a candle and a cup

Joy realised that the candle emitted light, and that the light travelled from the candle and entered her eye. However, she was not aware that objects also scatter light. She thought that as the cup obviously did not emit light, her eye must be actively sending out light instead and so she drew the light travelling from her eye to the cup. Holding two different models of vision presented no problem to Joy, as she focused only on aspects of the situation that she could see. To help Joy to realise that the way in which she could see both the candle and the cup was the same, her teacher asked her if she thought she would be able to see the cup when it was dark. She thought not and was able to test this by shutting herself and the cup in the stock cupboard. When it was dark in there she could not see the cup and when it was light she could. This caused Joy to re-consider her idea that her eye was sending out the light and to decide that she needed a source of light in order to see.

Using children's ideas

The influence of children's existing ideas on their learning is becoming increasingly recognised. As teachers, we need to know how the children in our classes view the world and think about science, so that we can take account of their thinking when designing and assessing their learning experiences. This requires us to adapt our teaching so that all children can engage with the ideas that they hold. By starting with the children's ideas, we can challenge them and provide experiences that will encourage new learning. As learning involves the children in actively restructuring their existing ideas and understandings in order to construct new meanings, it is unrealistic to expect them simply to absorb a 'right answer' or new idea imparted to them. They need time in which to discuss what they have done and found out, to reflect on the stability of their existing ideas, and to consider the need to change.

We can find out for ourselves what ideas the children in our classes hold by

1 listening to children's ideas
2 observing children at work
3 looking at children's drawings
4 inviting children to write about their ideas.

1 Listening to children's ideas

We spend enormous amounts of time listening to children, but on the whole most of us listen very poorly, although we often manage to delude ourselves that we are truly listening. Take a moment to recall a recent conversation you had with a child and consider whether you:

- pretended to listen while carrying on as best you could with what you were doing
- appeared to give attention by making comments at appropriate intervals
- listened selectively and pricked up your ears at some significant remark
- wondered how you could get the conversation over as quickly as possible or redirected in a more satisfactory way.

To listen properly to what children are saying requires effort and concentration, as we have to set aside our existing pre-occupations and shift our consciousness to try to understand them. This means we have to give up our own prejudices and frames of reference for the time being so as to experience as far as possible the children's point of view. So listening to children is not an easy option, but is one that enables us to find out what ideas they have so that we can set them appropriate tasks and assess their learning.

a Eavesdropping

Children's talk among themselves is more likely to reflect what they are actually thinking, rather than what they think the teacher wants to hear them say. While two six year olds carefully watched a candle burning, they were overheard expressing the following ideas:

George: *Candles are made of plastic.*

Mary:　*The stuff that drips off them is water.*

George: *When the water goes hard it goes white.*

Mary:　*When the water goes on the tray it dries up.*

Through questioning them their teacher may have discovered that George thought candles were made of plastic and Mary thought the stuff that dripped off them was water, but it is unlikely that she would have found out that George thought that 'water' dripped off the candle and went hard and white whilst Mary thought it dried up. Having overheard those remarks their teacher planned further activities that encouraged the children to compare water and melted candle wax. By putting water and melted wax separately on a tray and observing them they found out that the wax went hard and white but the water did not; and, when left for a few days, the water dried up but the wax did not. The children then discussed what they had done and found out and reviewed and modified their original ideas.

b Meanings of words

The meanings we give to words are based on our previous experiences of them. Sometimes subtly different meanings may be given to, or intended by, the same word when it is used by different people. Unfortunately when this happens in the classroom the child or teacher may not be aware that there is a difference, as the child believes he has understood or is understood, and so does the teacher. In discussion with some ten year olds a teacher was using the word 'bacteria' by which she meant 'organisms that are found in the soil and are concerned in the decay of plant and animal tissue'. To her surprise, she discovered that the children thought that bacteria were:

Lisa:　　　　*things what make things last longer*

Leanne:　　　*germs found in mouldy food*

Adam: *stuff on your teeth*

Christopher: *black spots*

Deborah: *things that will make you ill*

Damian: *something that makes your teeth dirty*

When we are talking and listening to children we, and they, may need to explore the meanings of the words that we are using in order to clarify them. We can do this by asking the children what they think a word means and then suggesting that they look it up in a dictionary to check if their meaning is the generally accepted one; or by giving the children a list of possible meanings and asking them to underline the one that they think is correct, before once again checking in a dictionary.

c Brainstorming

Some words have an everyday and a scientific usage that are subtly different. Collecting together a group of seven and eight year olds' ideas about force allowed their teacher to discover the range of ideas that they held. She was careful not to judge or sensor their ideas, so that the children felt that they could make any comment without fear of ridicule or disapproval.

- *action force*
- *it's there when something moves*
- *it gets used up when a toy car stops moving*
- *armed force*
- *police force*
- *lollipop ladies force cars to stop*
- *gravity's a force what pulls you down*

The children then arranged their ideas into two groups. They distinguished how the word was being used and in one group they put the ideas about force that were used in an everyday sense and in the other group those ideas that had something to do with the way in which force was used in a scientific sense.

d Discussion

When talking amongst themselves as well as with the teacher, children think aloud and make their ideas clearer to themselves as well as others, as they make possibly several attempts to describe their ideas, use language more precisely, evaluate their own and others' ideas and develop ideas further. As discussion may be constrained by the children's verbal skills, peer group and self-esteem, children need to learn how to discuss, how to present their own point of view and how to comment sensitively on the views of others.

To find out the ideas that two eight year olds held about air being all around us, a student teacher asked them what would happen when she took the lid off an apparently empty jam-jar.

Kirsty: *Air'd go in.*

Tony: *It can't, can it ? There's air in there already so how's more air going to fit in?*

Kirsty: *It's empty. There's nothing in there.*

Tony: *No it's not. There's air in there.*

Kirsty: *How do you know there's air in there? You can't see it.*

Tony: *Er... well... no, you can't see it but air's all around us, so it must be in the jar as well.*

Kirsty: *Well, maybe some air'll come out so some more can go in.*

Tony: *Why would it? Why'd some air come out so some more can go in?*

Kirsty: *Air moves round. It doesn't stay still. Like when I'm breathing. I'm breathing in and I'm breathing out and the air moves in and out of me, so it might move in and out the jar.*

These children listened to each other's points of view, and when they did not agree were able to challenge each other to explain further so that they were then in a better position to consider and evaluate the other's idea.

e Questioning

Asking questions in order to find out about children's ideas is difficult. Quite often we use questioning not to find out, but to give instructions – "Can you use a metre stick to measure that, do you think?" If we want to find out the ideas that children hold, we will need to ask them open-ended and productive questions, so that they can give any answer that they feel is appropriate and we avoid the 'right answer' approach. This means that we should not always expect an instant response as they may need time to consider their answer.

In order to discover children's ideas, we need to think carefully about how we phrase our questions, as a teacher doing some research found when she asked different questions to two groups of five year olds. Those who were asked "What can you tell me about magnets?"

expressed a range of ideas about magnets being made of metal, sticking to things, being able to push each other away if two magnets were held one way round and pull each other together if they were held the other way round, being different shapes and strengths, being used in toys and games, and being used to sort tin cans. Whereas a group in a parallel class who were asked "What do magnets do?" only expressed ideas about magnets sticking to a variety of objects.

Different types of questions can help children develop particular skills and encourage them to express alternative ideas. The following are examples of questions that can help to develop skills of:

i   measurement

Are the balls bouncing differently? In what ways?

How often will you need to make your measurements? What difference will it make if you measure at different times / lengths etc.?

How could you measure which one is stronger?

ii   observation

What did you notice happening when you added the water?

How is it actually moving?

What did you see through the magnifying glass that you couldn't see without it?

iii   comparison

What is the same / different about these leaves?

How could these materials be sorted into groups?

Why does the ammonite go in that set?

iv   prediction

What do you think will happen if you make the slope longer?

Which shape hull do you think will go fastest?

What could you change to reduce the friction?

v   problem solving

How could you make the light brighter?

Can you think of a way of measuring how windy it is?

How can you keep the tea warm?

vi   reasoning

Why do you think the ladybird is alive?

Why does the nail go rusty?

Can you explain why your boat floated and Timmy's didn't?

It is a good idea to repeat to the children the answers that they have given to questions, as it enables them, and the teacher, to check that they have said what they meant to say, as well as encouraging them to elaborate on the answer if they wish. It also provides an opportunity for other children to say what they think was meant and to add their own confirmation or contradiction of the answer.

Teacher: *You think your boat floated because of the material you used. Yours was made of polystyrene and that's waterproof and Timmy's was made of cardboard that isn't.*

Simon: *Yea, and Timmy's boat went soggy and split and the water got in.*

Timmy: *It went soggy first. That made it split and the water got in through the split and then it sank.*

2 Observing children at work

Observing children's actions while they are carrying out a task lets us see how they do it, whether they change their minds about what they are doing, how they test their ideas, and how they share them with others; and this provides more information than merely looking at the product of an activity, or what has been written about it.

Seven year olds Hanif and Eddy were testing materials for conductivity by using a simple electric circuit consisting of a battery, lamp, wires and the material to be tested.

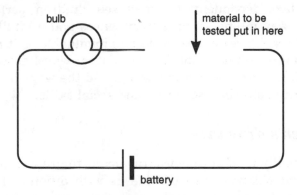

Figure 3.2 A simple electric circuit

They started by testing things that were already on their table: a ruler, a piece of paper and a pair of scissors. They discovered that the ruler and the paper did not light up the bulb. Eddy picked up the scissors and tested them by fixing one crocodile clip to the metal blades and one crocodile clip to one of the plastic covered handles. He discarded the scissors when he found that the bulb would not light up and got up and went off to look for more things to test. Hanif picked up the scissors and tested them as Eddy had done, and then tested them by fixing both crocodile clips to the plastic covered handles, and then tested them again by fixing both crocodile clips to the blades. Hanif called Eddy back and showed him that he had found out that the blades lit up the bulb. Eddy again went to look for things to test. Hanif, meanwhile, picked up the crocodile clips and tried fixing them to the black metal table legs. Eddy came back with a paper clip, a biro with a shiny metal clip, and a screw - all the items were shiny and silver coloured. Eddy immediately grabbed the apparatus and tested the things he had found and then said he would tell the teacher that they had finished. Hanif showed him that the table legs could light up the bulb. Eddy got very excited, picked up the apparatus and started testing the black plastic back of the chair. Hanif explained very carefully to him that it was metal things, not coloured things, that were lighting up the circuit and the pair of them went round the classroom looking for metal things to test.

If their teacher had only seen the list of things they found which conducted electricity, she would not have appreciated the way Hanif systematically worked it out, how he had influenced Eddy, or how Eddy had little understanding of conductivity and still needed to test his ideas. Observing children working is obviously time-consuming and is perhaps not something we feel able to spare much time to do when there are so many other demands on us in a busy classroom. It is also context dependent: we may see children performing an activity one way in one set of circumstances and a totally different way in another. However, observation is invaluable as it provides us with information, often unobtainable in other ways, about the ideas that the children are using and testing, and the ways in which they are developing both their scientific and social skills.

3   Children's drawings

Children usually need little encouragement to draw or paint. Their drawings and paintings can provide us with different information depending on the way in which we initially set up the task. This method of ascertaining children's ideas can be particularly useful with young children and children whose linguistic skills are limited, although, of course, it relies instead on their motor skills.

a Drawings as observations
In order to draw a three-dimensional object in two dimensions,

children have to learn to observe accurately and be disciplined enough to draw what they actually see and not what they think they see. Observational drawings can provide us with information about their ideas of scale and space, and how they see the various parts of an object fitting together to form a whole.

Dominic had been continually encouraged by his teacher to look and draw carefully. He was only five years old, but had already developed considerable skill, as his drawing of the bones of the human foot shows.

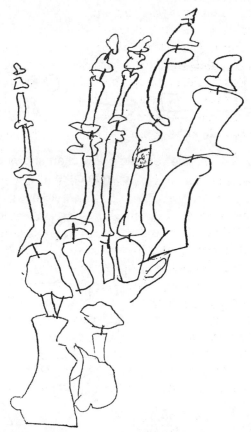

Figure 3.3   The bones of the human foot

Dominic had looked at and drawn from a real skeleton, hence the wires between the bones. He had noticed the way in which the bones fitted together, that they tapered towards the end of the toes, how the bones were shaped, and that there were similarities and differences between the shapes and sizes of the bones. He had not only observed but understood a lot about the structure of the foot and the way in which it worked.

b Drawings of how the world works

Flow charts and comic-strip pictures are a useful way in which to record the stages in a process or sequences of events, or to record changes that occur over a period of time, as they can be added to at intervals.

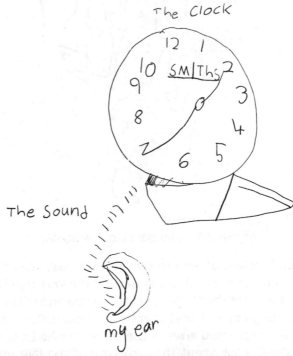

Figure 3.4 A nine year old's flow chart showing the transition of corn to cake

Figure 3.5 A six year old's drawing of how she was able to hear the sound of the clock ticking

Asking children to draw how they think something is made or works provides them with an opportunity to concentrate on function and relationships. Hannah, aged six, was asked by her teacher to draw how she was able to hear the sound of the clock ticking (figure 3.5).

Hannah's drawing shows that she thinks that the sound is travelling from the clock to her ear, that the sound travels in one direction only, that the sound is not continuous but comes at regular intervals, and that she uses her ear to hear. Hannah clearly had some ideas about the transmission and reception of sound. She was able to test and develop them when her teacher provided her with opportunities to find out if she could still hear the sound when she stood in different places in the room, and when one or both of her ears were covered. She was later able to check if her findings were applicable to other sounds that came at regular intervals, as well as sounds that she could hear continuously.

c Drawings as expressions of non-visual ideas

Children sometimes find it difficult to talk about abstract ideas or ideas of why they think something is happening, particularly when they cannot actually see it happen. However, just because it is abstract or they cannot see it happening does not mean that they have no ideas about it. Drawing or painting such ideas can often help children to clarify their thoughts and to use their pictures to help them express their ideas to others. They can be used by the teacher as a starting point to help the children to test the validity of their ideas.

Tom, aged ten, expressed his ideas about washing drying in his picture of a pair of tights hanging on a line (figure 3.6).

Tom knew that water dripped from the tights on to the ground to form small puddles. He also knew that the puddles disappeared. In order to explain where the water from the puddles went, he drew arrows showing that the water moved from the puddles into the sun. His teacher used this picture to challenge and extend Tom's ideas by asking him: What would happen to the water in the puddles if it was a cloudy day? How does the washing dry after it has stopped dripping? What difference does it make where you put the washing to dry? Tom was encouraged to devise and carry out a fair test to dry some washing under different conditions in order to find out about other factors, such as wind, heat and humidity that are involved in drying washing. He then used this information to investigate some puddles in order to find out if there were any common factors involved in the drying process and, as a result, was able to work towards a more scientific understanding of evaporation.

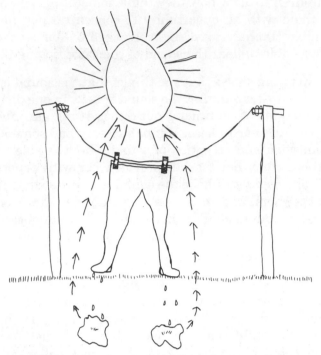

Figure 3.6   A pair of tights drying on a line

d Drawings as plans

Drawings are a useful way of helping children to clarify their ideas about planning an activity and sequencing the order of events, before they actually carry it out. By encouraging a systematic and logical approach, we can help children appreciate the processes involved in a scientific investigation, or in drafting step-by-step guides. They can then test and evaluate others' plans or guides by exchanging drawings and trying to construct what is shown.

Five year old Thomas drew the stages necessary to make a bulb, a bulb holder, two wires with crocodile clips, a battery and a battery holder into an electric circuit (figure 3.7).

He shows the steps clearly and has paid attention to details, such as the screw thread on the bulb, the screws on the bulb holder, the 'teeth' of the crocodile clip and the orientation of the battery. As he drew this picture before making the circuit, Thomas had to recall his previous experience of electric components and his knowledge of electric circuits, and to think carefully about the order in which he would carry out the task. His drawing shows the stages so clearly that other children were able to make a circuit following Thomas' instructions, thus validating his ideas.

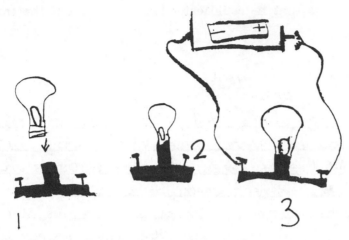

Figure 3.7   How to make an electric circuit

4 Children's writing

Writing is another way in which children can demonstrate their ideas. They are sometimes unwilling to express their ideas aloud, but will put them on paper. Such ideas may be ones that are only partially formulated, or ideas about which they feel strongly but are unable to discuss for some reason (death of a pet, for instance). Any writing is, of course, limited by the children's motor skills and their ability to express themselves on paper. In science we need to give children opportunities to write for different purposes and a variety of audiences, as this will provide different information about their ideas. This includes:

a Sustained writing
In this sustained and unprompted writing by eight year old John (figure 3.8), we can see evidence of his ideas about the different types and sources of energy, the uses of energy, and how energy is made. He clearly has had rich and varied experiences of energy from which he has been able to draw and has the ability to express himself with humour. This piece of writing also provided his teacher with many starting points to promote the development and extension of his ideas about energy. She encouraged him to find out more about renewable and non-renewable energy sources and the differences between them. She asked him: How do we get energy from food and drink? Does a bike or pram have energy only when we give it to them? The television uses electrical energy; what different types of energy are produced by it? He also looked at other electrical

appliances in order to find out the different types of energy they produced so that he could extend his ideas about the transfer of energy.

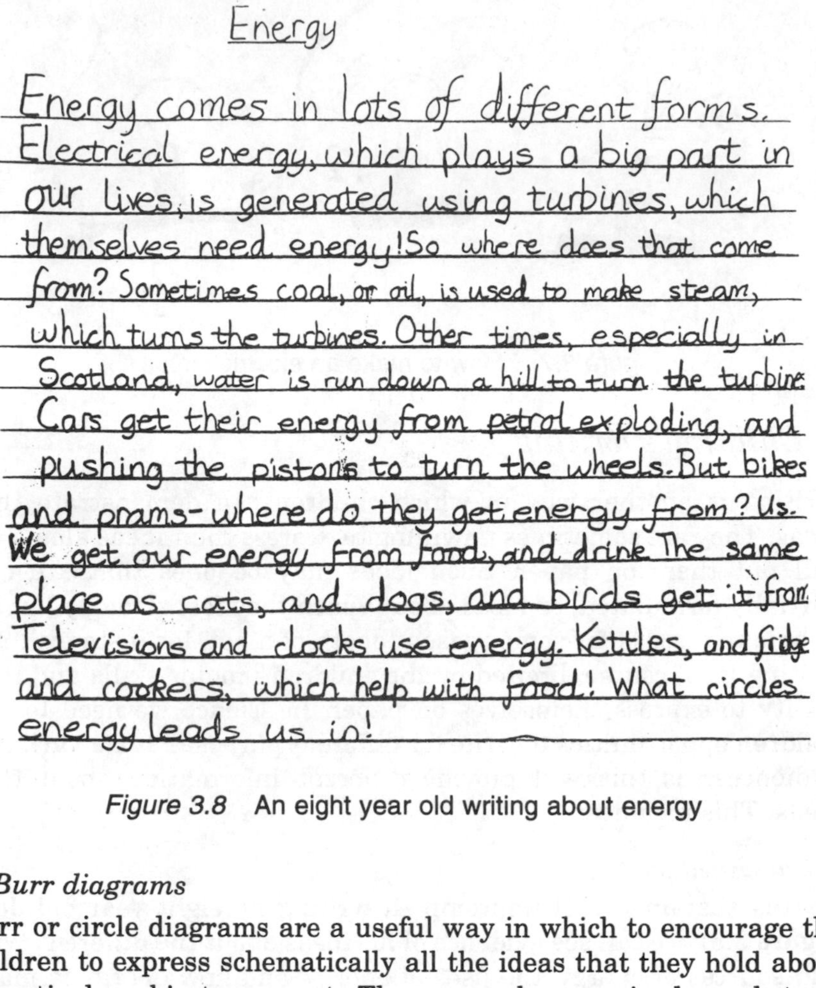

Energy

Energy comes in lots of different forms. Electrical energy, which plays a big part in our lives, is generated using turbines, which themselves need energy! So where does that come from? Sometimes coal, or oil, is used to make steam, which turns the turbines. Other times, especially in Scotland, water is run down a hill to turn the turbine. Cars get their energy from petrol exploding, and pushing the pistons to turn the wheels. But bikes and prams - where do they get energy from? Us. We get our energy from food, and drink. The same place as cats, and dogs, and birds get it from. Televisions and clocks use energy. Kettles, and fridge and cookers, which help with food! What circles energy leads us in!

Figure 3.8   An eight year old writing about energy

b Burr diagrams

Burr or circle diagrams are a useful way in which to encourage the children to express schematically all the ideas that they hold about a particular object or event. These may be perceived or abstract features or word associations, and may or may not be relevant, but are nonetheless linked in the children's minds because of their previous experiences.

Before starting a topic about mini beasts, Myra, age six, drew a burr diagram to show what she understood by the word 'animal' (figure 3.9).

Myra explained to her teacher that mini beasts could eat and move, but they were not animals because they were not furry and did not have four legs. They were just mini beasts. Animals were cats and dogs and the class hamster. Myra, like many young children, had a prescribed meaning for the word 'animal'. Myra's ideas were challenged by providing her with a range of mini beasts to study, after which she was able to identify certain characteristics that mini beasts had in common. She also began to realise that some of those characteristics were common not only to cats, dogs and the hamster but to other creatures too, and began to widen her ideas about animals.

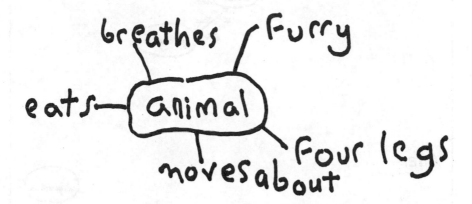

Figure 3.9   A six year old's burr diagram for 'animal'

c Concept maps
Concept maps can give us insights into children's ideas about the relationships between things. They are made by linking words that relate, showing the direction of the link by an arrow and writing a word, or phrase, along the arrow to indicate the reason for the link. For instance:

a cress seed   can grow   a root
------------------------➤

This very simple map tells us something about the relationship between the seed and the root. It is a starting point and could be expanded to encompass other relationships.

These two concept maps (figure 3.10) were drawn by ten year old Sam before and after she had worked on activities to do with temperature; they show that she had extended her ideas. Sam was encouraged to evaluate her own learning by identifying the differences between the two maps and considering the changes in her ideas.

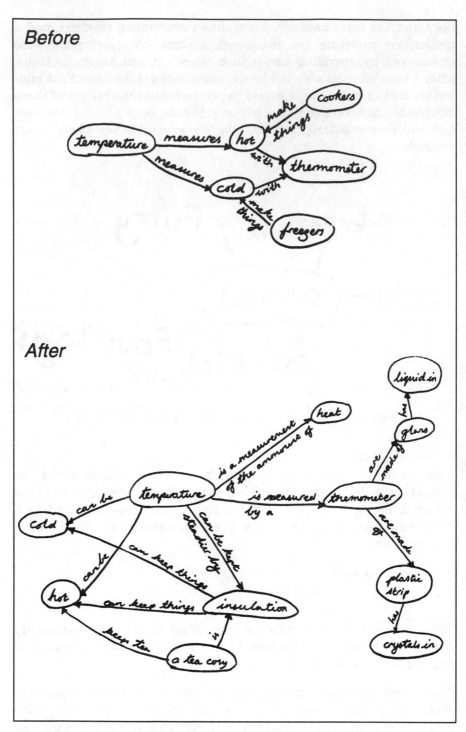

Figure 3.10 Sam's concept maps drawn before and after she carried out activities to do with temperature

The actual words used and the children's ability to read and write can influence the drawing of their maps. Very young children can be given the words written on separate pieces of card (with a picture clue if possible). The children can work in pairs to link the words with cardboard arrows and explain to each other why they are linking them.

Problem solving

To solve a problem, children have to recognise that there is a problem that needs solving. By asking children to find a solution to a problem (either practically or theoretically) we can gain some understanding of the ideas they have. However, it is not enough simply to set the children a task. To make it meaningful it is also important to link it with a need that arises from a context or situation that the children themselves recognise. This means that we will have to be open-minded and prepared to accept the children's way of going about it, and not insist that they adopt the method or the solution that we had in mind.

In a discussion that occurred during a topic on bicycles, nine year old Kiri wanted to know what would happen if she got oil on her brakes.

Amanda: *It'll make the brakes all wet and messy.*

Daniel: *They won't work so well.*

Kiri: *Why not?*

Daniel: *'Cos they'll be all slippy.*

Kiri: *Slippy?*

Amanda: *Yea, my Granddad oils things when they're all stuck to make them go better.*

Kiri: *So my brakes'll work better?*

Daniel: *No, they won't!*

Kiri: *But she* (pointing to Amanda) *just said they would.*

Daniel appeared to be trying to impose his view on the others, and so their teacher asked him to set up a demonstration to show the others what would happen if oil did get onto the brakes, and to explain why it mattered. However, Amanda's point of view was one that was also worth pursuing, and so the teacher asked her to find some things that were stuck, so that she could show the others how oiling them would help. As a result of these two activities Kiri, Amanda and

Daniel were able to develop their ideas about friction. They then looked at a bicycle and identified places where they thought it was a good idea to put oil in order to reduce friction.

To avoid frustration we may have to help the children to re-phrase a problem, or to split it into smaller and more manageable chunks. For example, "How can I stop my bike going rusty?" may need to be broken down into smaller problems first, as it requires the children to have some understanding of the types of materials that rust and where those materials are on a bike. They will also need to have some understanding of the factors that cause rusting and the ways in which the rusting process can be slowed, before they can consider a way that would be an appropriate one for them to use on the parts of their bikes that are liable to rust.

Summary

Every method of finding out about children's ideas has its strengths and its limitations. By using a variety of methods we can acquire a wider range of information. However, no matter what method we use, we need to show children that we take their ideas seriously, as well as providing them with a supportive atmosphere in which they can express and change their ideas without being made to feel that they are wrong. Children also need time for reflection if they are to develop their ideas further. They may not change or develop their ideas quickly, or may not change their ideas at all or make the links that we intend. 'Re-visits' provide opportunities for the children to review, consolidate and develop the ideas that they hold. After any teaching we need to find out what ideas the children now hold, so that we can plan the next teaching and learning to challenge and extend those ideas.

4 Evidence of children's learning in science

Some circumstantial evidence is very strong, as when you find a trout in the milk.

H D Thoreau, *Miscellanies*

Much of the information that we gain about how children view the world, and the ideas that they hold and use, can be recorded in order to provide evidence of their learning at that point. This evidence can then be used as a basis for:

- reporting to others (parents, other teachers, support staff, etc.)
- evaluating and informing our teaching and the children's learning
- planning the next steps in the children's learning.

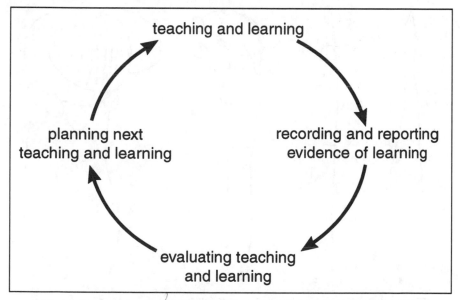

Figure 4.1   The cyclical nature of teaching and learning

Recording learning

The recording of children's learning has, of necessity, to be done at an individual level and within a specific context, if its purpose is to provide us with accurate and useful evidence of each child's thinking to which we and others such as parents, advisers, psychologists and other support staff can refer. The recording of such information can also provide us with evidence that can be compared with the children's past learning or their learning in different situations or subjects and can enable us to consider ways in which the children might be helped to improve their performance and build on their achievements. As such these records should not be judgmental but simply factual accounts of each child's attainment.

Although the recording is individual, the evidence is often easier to gather from children working together and talking about what they are doing. We can obtain and record evidence of the children's learning through:

1 looking at the results of the children's everyday work
2 making observations, listening to them, questioning them and so on when they are carrying out activities
3 testing the children.

1 *Children's work*

1   2   3   4

Figure 4.2   Four drawings of a daffodil flower done by four year old
Rebecca as she learnt to observe more closely

Much of the children's normal classwork will provide permanent records of their learning in the form of writing, drawings, charts and so on. If similar but increasingly demanding learning experiences are repeated at intervals and the resulting work dated, it can be used to provide evidence of the children's learning and will show the progress that they have made.

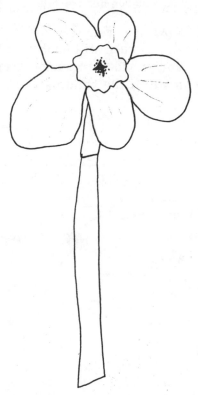

Figure 4.3   Five year old Rebecca's drawing of a daffodil

Rebecca, aged four, had only been in the reception class two weeks when her teacher gave her an open daffodil flower and asked her to draw it. Drawing 1 (Figure 4.2) is the first attempt she made. However, this activity was overseen by a student teacher who encouraged her to look more closely and carefully at the daffodil and to try to draw what she actually saw (Drawing 2). The student teacher then questioned Rebecca about the shape of the flower head, as a result of which she attempted to draw the petals and trumpet separately (Drawing 3). Finally the student teacher suggested that Rebecca looked inside the trumpet and included what she saw there in her drawing (Drawing 4). Although the four drawings were done with a pencil and only took Rebecca a few minutes to complete, they had provided her with an opportunity to learn about the structure of the flower and the importance of drawing what she actually saw (and not what she imagined). Obviously the student teacher's contribution was a vital encouragement to Rebecca's learning and emphasises the impact of appropriately timed teaching. Rebecca's next drawings of flowers, although done without any intervention by her teacher, were less sketchy than those of the daffodil and showed more attention to detail. When, a year later, Rebecca again drew a daffodil flower, her drawing showed that she had made considerable progress with her drawing skills and her ability to observe accurately.

Many of the ways outlined in previous chapters will be part of the children's normal classwork and as such will enable us to find out about the children's thinking and provide permanent records of their learning. Some other ways in which the children can record their work in science include:

a Evidence of observation

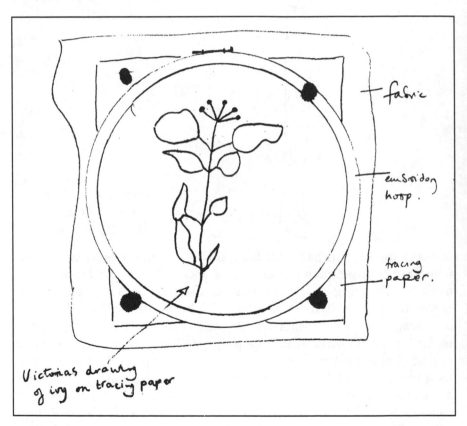

Figure 4.4   Five year old Victoria's drawing of ivy ready for embroidery

Embroidery   Embroidery is a useful method of encouraging children to observe closely and to match colours precisely, particularly if they are allowed to choose the embroidery threads or wools that they use for themselves. A simple way by which young children can be helped to learn to embroider is for them to draw the object under observation on a piece of thin paper. Clear outline pencil drawings with not too many small details or shadings work best. A drawing that the child has already done in his book can be traced onto grease proof paper for embroidery.

The drawing is then pinned, tacked or fixed with sellotape, paper clips or an embroidery hoop onto a piece of fabric. The embroidery is worked through both paper and fabric simultaneously, following the lines of the drawing. An unbroken line of stitching looks best, and inexperienced embroiderers can achieve this by using a simple running stitch worked in one direction and then back in the opposite direction in order to fill in the gaps. When the stitching is complete the paper is torn away so that the embroidery is then on the fabric. Any fragments of paper remaining under stitches can be teased out with a needle.

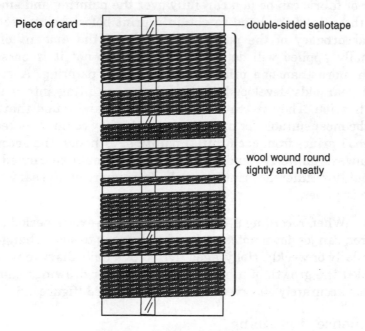

Figure 4.5   A wool winding

Wool windings Wool windings are another way of encouraging children to observe closely and to match colours precisely. They need to look very carefully at an object to notice the variety and number of colours of which it is composed. They may be surprised to discover that, for example, a blue eye is not simply a single shade of blue. The children can then select wools of all the colours in the object. Lengths of wool are then wound as neatly as possible onto a piece of card about 4 cm wide by 10 cm long, that has double-sided sellotape (or a loop of ordinary sellotape) down the length of one side to hold the wool in place. The amount of each colour of wool wound should be roughly proportional to the amount of that colour in the object.

Printing   Printing also allows the children to mix paints or printing inks in order to achieve a good colour match with an object. While this can of course be done with ordinary painting, printing has the advantage that when wrongly mixed colours have been used they can be wiped out and replaced by a better match before the piece is printed. It is not necessary to have access to screen printing equipment or even to make a printing block in order to be able to print. At a very simple level printing can be realised by painting the mixed colours onto a piece of smooth shiny material such as Formica or perspex. A piece of rag or paper towel can be used to remove any mistakes. When the shape and colours are satisfactory, a piece of paper or fabric can be laid carefully over the painting and smoothed with the side of the hand to obtain a print before being peeled off. The absorbency of the paper or fabric and the amount of paint originally applied will determine whether or not it is possible to obtain more than one print from the initial painting. A group of seven year olds developed this method of printing into a science investigation. They tested a range of fabrics and found that cotton was the most suitable for printing and that they could repeatedly get two good prints from each initial painting, although the second one was always fainter. A similar investigation could be carried out to find out how different printing methods compare on the same type of fabric or paper.

Diary   When recording events that take place over a period of time, children can jot down notes and make sketches to show changes that occur daily or weekly. Holly, aged five, kept a daily diary in which she recorded the growth of a broad bean seed. Her drawings show that she has accurately observed the developing seed (figure 4.6).

b Evidence of planning

Planning sheets   The use of planning sheets has become more widespread since the introduction of the National Curriculum required all children to undertake investigative science. Planning sheets provide both children and teachers with a framework before investigation and a means of recording afterwards. However, any planning sheet should not be used too rigidly and may need to be

Figure 4.6 Five year old Holly's diary of growing broad beans

adapted to the needs of the children and the investigation in hand. A typical planning sheet has various headings that the children need to consider, and the teacher can encourage them to do this by asking them questions that help them to focus on specific issues. For example, the following planning sheet (pp 78-9) is one devised by a teacher of ten year olds and used individually by the children.

Group books Individual planning sheets are not suitable for very young children and may be rather daunting for children who have difficulty in expressing themselves in writing. Also as children need to learn to be flexible and creative in their approach to investigations, it is not appropriate to use planning sheets for every investigation. Purpose made, large-sized books can provide an alternative method of recording the ideas that a group of children hold and use when planning their investigations. They are

Our investigation into...

The people who took part were...

We are investigating...

What have you decided to find out about?

How could you test that?

Variables we have identified in our investigation

How are you going to make sure it is a fair test?

Which of these have you decided to change? (the independent variable)

Which of these have you decided to keep the same? (the control variables)

Which of these are you going to measure? (the dependent variable)

How will you measure it?

Our prediction

What do you think will happen if you do that?

Why do you think that will happen?

Other things to think about

What equipment / time / space will you need?

How are you going to share the various tasks between you?

What will you need to do to carry out your investigation safely?

How will you record the results?

What we did

What did you actually do?

What did you notice?

What did you measure?

Our results

Why do you think your results are reliable?

Can you think of a better way to record your results?

What is the unit of measurement?

Where is the explanation for the symbols you have used?

What we found out

What can you tell me about your investigation?

Why do you think that happened?

Was your investigation a valid one?

What do your results mean?

Do you notice any pattern in your results?

Have you learnt any new / special words in this investigation?

Have you found out what you thought you were going to find out?

The next step is....

Is there any way in which you could have improved your investigation?

How are you going to let other people know what you have been doing?

What do you need to do next / find out about next as a result of your investigation?

particularly useful for work carried out over a period of time as they can be displayed next to the investigation, to act as reminders of the children's questions and what they had decided to do.

Large sheets of paper can be folded and stapled or sewn to make a big book or concertinaed to form a zig-zag book. At the top of the first page a question is written in such a form that it encourages the children to express their ideas. Three six year olds who were asked "What do we already know about rusting?" responded with: "It makes things go orangey", "Only metal things rust", "Rusty nails are dangerous", "My bike's going rusty 'cos it has to stay out in the rain" and "Things don't rust if you keep them dry". All of the children's replies were written on the first page of the book by the teacher and each child put his name or initials against his own idea. In response to one of the ideas generated by the initial question, the teacher wrote on the second page: "How could we find out if it is true that things always go orangey when they rust?" Again all the answers were written down and the children encouraged to choose one of the suggestions to develop into an investigation that they then planned in detail on subsequent pages by answering questions such as, "What will we need?" "What do we think will happen?" "How will we make sure it is a fair test?" and so on.

Wall displays　Group planning of an investigation can be presented on a large scale as a wall display. This is a useful way to create impact and stimulate interest. Although planned and investigated collectively, each child in the group can be responsible for one aspect of the final presentation. This will obviously require co-operation particularly if the children mount the wall display themselves, as they will have to make sure that they have thought about, and where necessary agreed on, issues such as:

• the size and shape of the wall available
• method of presentation (written, drawn, painted or a combination of methods)
• colour, style and size of writing
• mounting and backing papers
• the sequencing of the display.

The children may find it useful to have planned their investigation under headings such as:

• *Blue group's investigation into...*
• *What we already knew about this was...*
• *We predicted that...*
• *What we decided to do was...*

- *We carried out a fair test by...*
- *Our results were...*
- *We found out that...*
- *Our evaluation of our investigation was...*

c Evidence of recording results

As children gradually begin to take more responsibility for planning their own investigations, opportunities arise for them to decide for themselves suitable ways in which they can record and present their results. Deciding how to present their results for themselves, trying, and being critical of what they have done, enables more learning than being instructed to "draw a graph" or "make a bar chart of your results". Children may need to be reminded that it is necessary to record results in some format so that they can be checked for reliability and used for drawing conclusions and communicating to others. They may also need support in order to try different methods of recording, to consider the appropriateness of the methods that they use, and to evaluate their results.

Even when children have planned their own investigation, they will not necessarily be able to perceive how it will work in practice. So how they determine to record their results will depend not only on their understanding of the purpose of their investigation but their perceptions of how it will work out. We may have to encourage them to consider what is likely to happen, so that they think about the most effective way of recording and communicating their data. They may also need help with thinking about the advantages and disadvantages of different ways of recording their results within the context of an investigation. Collecting and recording data in itself provides us with little evidence of the children's learning. However, the way in which they use the data that they collect and the conclusions that they draw from it can give us considerable information about their ideas.

Tables and spreadsheets The Assessment of Performance Unit suggested[1] that whilst children are able to represent data in graphs, tables and charts as an isolated activity, they often fail to apply these skills when carrying out investigations. Even when the children are able to choose and use the most appropriate way in which to record their investigative results, we may need to help them to consider the amount of data that it is necessary to record.

Collecting overwhelming amounts of data can be a potential difficulty when the children begin to use spreadsheets, as it is very easy for them to accumulate rows and columns of figures that they then cannot manipulate, or for which they have no use. Spreadsheets are often used to record the data collected in class surveys or events that occur over a period of time. For example, a group of nine year olds recorded the following weather data:

date	max. temp	min. temp	rainfall	total sun	av. wind speed
1.5	15°C	3°C	0	6.5 hours	Beaufort 3
2.5	12°C	4°C	1.5mm	3.25 hours	Beaufort 3
3.5	14°C	4°C	2.5mm	0	Beaufort 4
4.5	13°C	5°C	0.5mm	4 hours	Beaufort 2

When faced with quantities of data, the children may need to be shown how to analyse it in order to draw out the information that they require and how to simplify it so that they can more easily distinguish the patterns in that data. Andrew, who helped to collect the above data, found that he could more easily appreciate the difference between maximum and minimum temperatures by plotting them on the same graph (figure 4.7).

Products as a record Some explorations and investigations naturally lead to products other than written work as an end point, and these can also be useful records of the children's results. Such products may be charts, graphs, maps or models. A group of eight year old children who had investigated the different types and quantities of plants growing in two contrasting habitats, recorded their results as metre square maps. These maps were used by the children to draw conclusions about plant growth and to enable them to verify the hypotheses that they had put forward as the basis of their investigation (figure 4.8).

The way in which the children set up a model can also give us information about their learning. Two seven year old children had been investigating a range of materials to find one suitable for making a long bridge. Their teacher had evidence of their understanding of the properties of materials required for bridge building, as she heard them discussing aspects of strength, flexibility and length and observed their choice of materials. The model itself was a record of the results of their investigation and was photographed to provide a permanent record.

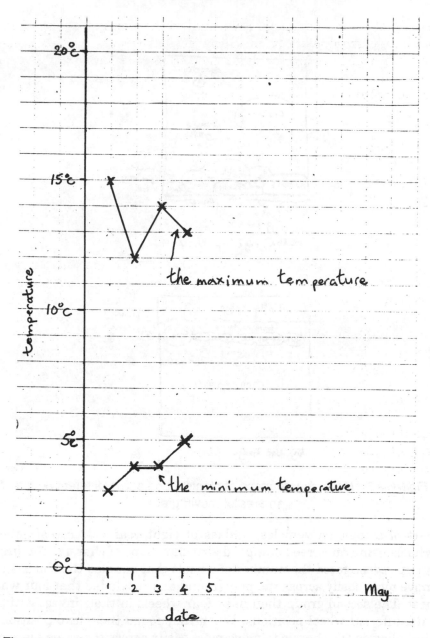

Figure 4.7 Andrew's graph of the maximum and minimum temperature, taken from the spreadsheet above

Using others' results The recording of their results allows children to check them for reliability, as well as drawing conclusions from them and communicating them to others. The importance of this may need to be emphasised when the children carry out investigations, the conclusions of which form the basis of further investigations. As

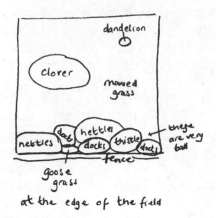

at the edge of the field

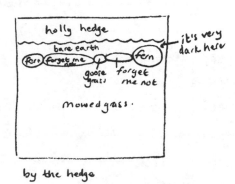

by the hedge

Figure 4.8   Metre square maps of plants found at two different edges of an area of mown grass

part of a topic on vehicles, a class of eight year olds investigated wheels using an agreed standard size and shape of chassis. The first group investigated the number of wheels that enabled the chassis to move most easily across the playground and concluded that four was best. The second group then used four wheels in their investigation into different wheel positions. When they found the wheel positions that allowed the chassis to move most easily across the same piece of playground, they passed the information to the third group who used the same wheel number and position and investigated a range of wheel sizes. A fourth group then used the information provided by the other groups, in their investigation into different types of materials for tyres. At the end of the investigations each group had contributed some information, so that a chassis was fitted with the combination of wheel number, position, size and tyre that enabled it to move most easily across the playground.

2 Teacher observations of children working

Some of the wide variety of everyday classwork that children undertake will provide information about their learning but will not be recorded by the children themselves. In such instances we may be able to record evidence of their learning by photographing the activity (such as the construction of an electric circuit) or the end product (a Lego car with flashing lights). If the activity or end product is not a suitable one for photography, observations about it can be noted instead. Of course it is not realistic to jot down observations about every activity that children undertake so we should select ones that contribute evidence of learning to a child's profile. The following example of a teacher's notes provided evidence of ten year old Tim's learning during a group activity to design and make a glider capable of covering as great a distance as possible.

Name: *Tim*   Date: 18.5.93
Activity: *designing gliders*
Evidence of learning:

- *trialled different triangular shapes*
- *considered proportions of width and length*
- *measured accurately in mm.*

Figure 4.9   A teacher's record of a ten year old's learning during a group activity

3 Testing

Tests of various kinds, whether formal or informal, can also provide permanent records of the children's learning. Traditionally short-recall type tests have often been given at the end of a topic to check if the children have learnt the necessary facts. This type of test often takes the form of:

- closed questions that require the correct answer (What is the unit that is used when measuring force?)

- providing some information in order to find out what the children can remember about it (Label as many things on this diagram of a plant as you can.)
- giving the children a number of possible answers to a question and requiring them to choose the correct one (Underline the right answer: A frog is (a) a fish (b) a reptile (c) an amphibian or (d) a mammal.)

Although this type of test can tell us whether or not the children have learnt the required facts, it gives us little information about the children's understanding, why they have chosen the answers that they have or how those answers link to their existing ideas about a subject. If we want evidence of the children's learning, then we will need to set up ways that make this possible. Possibilities include:

- open-ended questions that allow the children to express their knowledge (What can you tell me about solids?)
- concept maps that explore the connections that children make between the ideas that they hold (Link together as many of these words as you can: heart, lungs, blood, veins, oxygen, arteries. Explain why you think they link together.)
- annotated drawings (Draw what you think happens in the water cycle. Put notes on your drawing to explain what you think is going on.)
- providing statements and asking the children to explain why they agree or disagree with them (The earth goes round the moon. Do you agree? or disagree? Why?).

Evaluating teaching and learning

Teaching and learning are so closely inter-linked that it is difficult to separate them. Teaching informs learning; learning informs teaching. When we evaluate either teaching or learning we are expressing *what has been* taught or learnt in terms of *what we hoped had been* taught or learnt. Thus evaluating learning can be thought of as a process in which teachers look at the evidence of children's learning, strive to understand it, and then put that understanding to good use in their teaching. Similarly when we evaluate our teaching, we look at the evidence of the children's learning, reflect on the effectiveness of our teaching methods and schemes of work, and then plan the next learning and teaching steps as appropriate. This requires us to be completely honest and to put aside issues that may colour the facts, so that we can use our evaluations to improve both learning and teaching.

Evaluation of children's learning by the teacher

Teachers use the evidence of children's learning to try to understand their achievements and progress in skills and subject knowledge. In doing so they highlight the children's strengths and weaknesses, diagnose any learning difficulties and use this to inform their planning. Tim's teacher watched him designing and making a glider capable of covering as great a distance as possible and concluded that he was able to make relevant observations and measurements. She decided that the next step for Tim was systematically to collect and present his observations in a form that would provide him with an opportunity to look for patterns in his data and take account of those patterns when drawing conclusions about the relationship between the glider design and the distance it was able to cover.

The most common way in which children see teacher evaluation taking place in the classroom is in the marking of their work, whether it is a tick at the end of a piece of written work, a "Well done!" in response to practical work, or an invitation to the class to applaud. Children who are less sure of themselves and their abilities may ask for their work to be marked part way through in order to give them positive reinforcement that they are on the right track. This needs to be discouraged as it can set up the teacher as an expert in the child's eyes and he may become dependent on such a relationship. Instead of marking in this way, we can consider the work together with the child, thus creating an opportunity to talk about the work, explore the child's understanding, and consider what evidence there is for progression. Unlike marking this is a more extensive evaluation and one that both stimulates and records learning.

Evaluation of learning by children

Dependent learners always need the teacher to inform them. Effective learners are those who have learnt how to make use of the resources around them to stimulate their questions and their strategies for enquiry. A class of five year olds was to be introduced to electric circuits for the first time. Instead of taking the somewhat traditional approach with batteries, wires, light bulbs and crocodile clips, their teacher decided to start with torches. The children were divided into small groups and a different type of torch given to each group. Each group had time to take their torch to pieces, to find out about the various parts, how those parts fitted together and how the parts were all essential for the torch to work. They then made a list (written out by an adult) of what they had found about the torch.

What do we know about our torch?
- *It can shine a light.*
- *It's got two batteries inside.*
- *You press the switch and it comes on. You press the switch again and it goes off.*
- *The outside's rubber.*
- *There's a shiny metal bit behind the light.*
- *There's a spring inside what squashes the batteries in.*

After they had pooled their ideas about their torch, the children discussed with an adult what else they would like to find out about it and another list was made.

What do we want to find out about our torch?
- *Why does it matter what way you put the batteries in?*
- *Can you put in different size batteries?*
- *How does the switch know if you've pressed it to go on or if you've pressed it to go off?*
- *Does the bit behind the light have to be shiny?*

The children were very keen to find out the answers to these questions and became engrossed in thinking of ways in which they could do so. They were able to investigate and answer unaided all the questions except the one about the switch, as they could not see enough of the inside of the torch to find out how the switch worked. However, this gave the teacher the opportunity to take the bulb and batteries out of the torch and to join them with wires and clips to make a circuit. The children were then able to see how the light only came on when the circuit was complete and went off when the circuit was broken. They were then able to make their own pressure switch and to introduce other types of switches into the circuit. Next they explained to another group what they now understood about their torch (and particularly its switch!) and then reviewed their own learning by comparing what they now knew about the torch with their original list.

Independent learners need evidence of what they know and have found out as the result of an activity. A necessary component of an activity is, therefore, the recording and evaluating of their learning. It is important to encourage children to structure their evaluations so that they are constructive and not an opportunity to make negative remarks about others' abilities or performance. We can do this by focusing on specific issues such as:

- planning: *What did you know about this before you started? Were the questions you raised helpful?*
- method: *Are there any changes you think it would have been useful to have made to what you did? Why might that be? How would you do it differently another time?*
- results and conclusions: *Why do you think these results are reliable? Why do you think your investigation was valid? What makes you think these conclusions apply to what you have investigated? What have you learnt from this?*

Evaluation also encourages the children to make decisions about what they want to do and learn next. As learners interested in their own learning, they are more likely to become absorbed in activities that they find of interest and value, and to become stimulated to expand their endeavours, whatever their age. To do this they need time after carrying out a task to reflect on what they have done and how they have done it, to consider ways in which they can improve their performance, and what they think is appropriate for them to do next. Amanda, Chris, Adam, Russell and Michelle, all aged ten, opted to carry out a science investigation together. However, during the course of the investigation it became apparent that five people were really too many to be working together as a group. They recorded this at the end of the investigation (figure 4.10).

As the children had time after carrying out the investigation to evaluate their individual contributions to it and to draw their own conclusions about working together as a group, they chose smaller working groups for investigations from then on. Having the time in which to reflect on their performance and to record their evaluation of it was a crucial part of their learning, without which they would not have been as likely to have made changes to their way of working. If their teacher had made the decision about group size, they would not have appreciated that there is an optimum number for groups to operate effectively.

Planning next teaching and learning

When determining the next phase of the children's learning we need to consider what it is appropriate to teach and what learning can be expected from that teaching, as teaching and learning go hand in hand and need to be planned together. Whether planning the next day's or the next term's activities it is always useful to consider:

1 What ideas do the children already have about this?
2 What ideas do I think the children should work towards next?
3 What learning do I hope that they will gain from teaching about it?

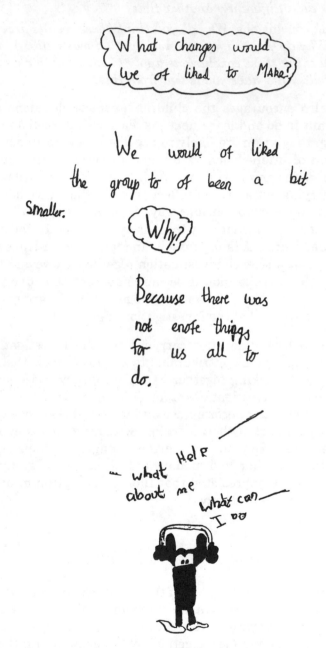

Figure 4.10 A group of ten year olds reflect on a way of improving their performance

In planning a half-termly topic on 'Ourselves', a teacher of five year olds decided to include teaching about foods. She asked herself:

1 "What ideas do the children already have about food?"

I'm not sure, but I can find out by talking to them, asking them to tell me their ideas, getting them to draw pictures of where specific foods come from etc.

The teacher took time to find out the ideas that the children held about food and concluded that they:

- *knew food came from shops, but not all the children realised that food was grown elsewhere before it arrived in the shops*
- *realised you had to eat food to stay alive, but did not realise that a balanced diet was necessary*
- *appreciated that some people in some countries do not have enough to eat, but "they eat funny things anyway"*
- *were not very aware of food hygiene.*

The teacher was then able to ask herself:

2 "What ideas about food do I think these children should work towards next?"

- *an appreciation of aspects of hygiene to do with food*
- *a realisation that there are different types of food and that they are all necessary for growth as well as life*
- *a respect for people whose diets are different from their own*
- *an awareness that food is not something to be taken for granted*

3 "What learning do I hope that the children will gain from this teaching about food?"

- *skills:*   *asking questions and suggesting ideas*
                      classifying
                      collecting and recording data
                      interpreting results

- *attitudes:*   *co-operation*
                      open-mindedness
                      curiosity
                      responsibility

- *increased*   *food types and origins*
  knowledge of: *relationship between food and growth*
                      keeping food, hands and utensils clean when preparing and serving food

At the end of the topic she evaluated her teaching and the children's learning by reflecting on the answers that she had made to her initial questions:

- *Did I provide the children with opportunities to find out about food hygiene?*
- *Did I provide the children with opportunities to find out about different food types and the relationship between food and growth?*
- *Have I encouraged the children to be more tolerant of other people's eating habits and diets?*
- *Have I encouraged the children to be more responsible in their attitude to food?*
- *What skills have the children developed as a result of the different activities?*
- *What attitudes have the children developed?*
- *How have their ideas altered as a result of the activities they did?*
- *What implications does this have for their future learning and my future planning?*
- *What am I going to do next to ensure that they build on their previous experiences and progress individually?*

APU survey findings

The evidence that we gain about the children's learning forms the basis on which we make decisions about what it is appropriate to teach next and the learning that can be expected from that teaching. It also allows us to consider if we can improve the children's learning by designing our teaching by some other way. The Assessment of Performance Unit was set up in the Department of Education and Science in order to provide information about children's achievements at school. The large-scale surveys conducted by the APU's science monitoring team recorded children's performance in science and the quality of their learning at the ages of 11, 13 and 15. Although this research was carried out in the 1980s, it is still valid and has implications for the ways in which we teach science to children throughout the primary school. The APU lists some suggestions[2] that we can consider when planning our science teaching:

- encourage children to design their own approaches to solving problems and allow them to try out their ideas
- discuss with the children the progress of their investigations and encourage them to discuss with each other

- discuss the children's results and challenge them to show how they were worked out from the evidence

- listen to children's ideas and probe their 'wrong' responses; encourage them to explain their reasons for their ideas; use this knowledge in planning further activities for the children

- help children to review critically their practical procedures and to consider alternative strategies for solving problems or investigating.

The APU's findings also highlight the fact that girls need to become more aware of the importance of taking measurements and of taking them accurately. Boys on the other hand may need more guidance than girls in recording what they have done in a systematic way and in describing their investigations so that others can understand the procedures that they followed.

The APU science team also suggest that girls may need more encouragement than boys to take an active part in science and to use scientific equipment. This is often compounded by the teacher planning the investigation and putting the equipment out ready for the children to use in order to 'save time'. Girls more than boys may recoil from apparatus that is already put out and that they find threatening (a set of pulleys, for instance), or do not understand how to use (a microscope) or think may hurt them in some way (a hack saw) and thus have an understandable reluctance to become involved. However, by encouraging and allowing girls to use their own ideas to plan their own investigations and to choose their own equipment we can help them to become not only active but keen participants. A girl who has decided for herself that she wants to collect aphids as her contribution to the class' minibeast collection, is far more likely to ask for help with using a pooter than a girl who is told "You take the pooter, Jan. Off you go."

Summary

Evidence of the children's thinking and learning can be gained and recorded by a variety of methods, can be shared with others and used to evaluate both our teaching and the children's learning. Such evidence is also a necessary basis for decisions about the next phase of the children's learning, as we need to use it to plan what is appropriate to teach next and the learning that can be expected from that teaching. The whole process of teaching and learning is a cyclical one that should be continually reviewed and updated. If the children's ideas form the basis of our teaching, we need to be able to find out how their ideas have altered as a result of any learning that has taken place, so that we can ensure that they build on their previous experiences and progress individually.

References

1 DES, *Science at Age 11: A Review of APU Survey Findings 1980-1984*, HMSO, London, 1988, p 39

2 DES, *Assessment of Performance Unit: Science Report for Teachers: 1 Science at Age 11*, HMSO, London, 1983, pp 12–13

5 Starting points for teaching and learning science

Education sets the exams that fit what it teaches and then prides itself that it has taught the right things for the exams.

Edward de Bono, *Po: Beyond Yes and No*

Education in the primary school is in danger of becoming attainment led as the National Curriculum has set standards of performance for the majority of children. In planning to teach science we need to look beyond the requirements of the National Curriculum in order to give the children a science education that provides them with a programme of experiences and activities from which they can construct meanings, make links with their previous scientific knowledge, and develop their scientific skills and attitudes. This may seem daunting for the non-specialist teacher. However, science is all around us and can be taught and learnt from the everyday classroom items and situations with which we are already familiar. Recognising the scientific potential of commonplace objects and activities is not always easy but, if we remember that primary science is a way of seeing, doing and thinking, we can more easily identify opportunities that we can develop. How we develop them into learning activities will depend on the children's previous experiences as well as their physical and mental skills, their motivation and needs.

Starting points for learning science

Everyday classroom activities such as painting, music making and story telling offer productive starting points for the teaching and learning of science. By drawing science out of familiar activities, we are able to emphasise two important factors:

1 that science is not a separate and discrete discipline but is integral to many aspects of everyday life

2 that the children can ask scientific questions in any context and
   that the context gives substance to those questions.

Young children rarely compartmentalise their ideas and by helping
them to form links between subjects we enable them to make greater
sense of their various learning experiences. Thus, for example, when
retelling the Bible story of Noah and the ark, a teacher of a vertically
grouped class of five to seven year olds asked questions that helped
the children to recognise some of the science in the story:

- *What different types of food do you think Noah might have
  needed to take with him to feed such a variety of animals?*
- *How do you think Noah might have got the animals from the
  land and onto the ark?*
- *What arrangements do you think Noah might have made for
  housing such a variety of animals?*
- *How do you think the ark was able to float with all those animals
  and all that food on board?*

There are no 'right' answers to these questions, but all the children
had ideas and were able to make suggestions. Some children had
seen things being pushed up ramps or winched onto ships. Others
had pets at home and realised that different animals have specific
feeding requirements. Several remembered seeing television
programmes and library books about carnivorous animals and
suggested that those should be housed apart from others. Some of
the children drew on their own experiences of putting on armbands
when learning to swim in order to make suggestions about floating.
The ideas that they expressed were not necessarily scientifically
accurate or complete, but were important to them and formed
starting points from which the teacher was able to help the children
to link scientific concepts to everyday life and to raise further
questions that they found of interest.

The children then collectively made a list of some of the different
animals that they thought might have been on board the ark. Their
teacher used this list as a starting point for developing the children's
individual ideas about the characteristics of animals, by asking them
each to think of a way of arranging the animals into groups. Amanda
and Jane grouped the same list of animals in different ways (figure
5.1).

Once this was done, Amanda and Jane each explained to the rest of
the class the criteria that they had used for grouping the animals
and the problems that they encountered in doing so (what to do about
dog, frog and snake). The class were then able to compare the criteria

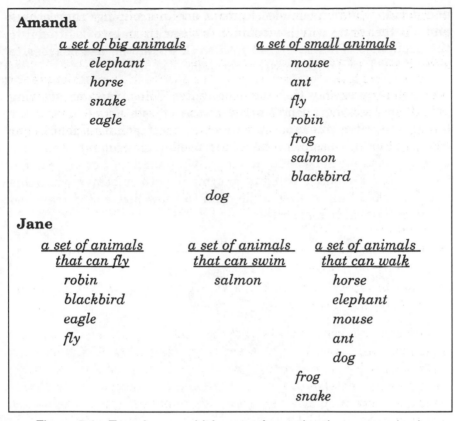

Amanda

a set of big animals	*a set of small animals*
elephant	mouse
horse	ant
snake	fly
eagle	robin
	frog
	salmon
	blackbird

dog

Jane

a set of animals that can fly	*a set of animals that can swim*	*a set of animals that can walk*
robin	salmon	horse
blackbird		elephant
eagle		mouse
fly		ant
		dog

frog
snake

Figure 5.1 Two six year olds' ways of grouping the same animals

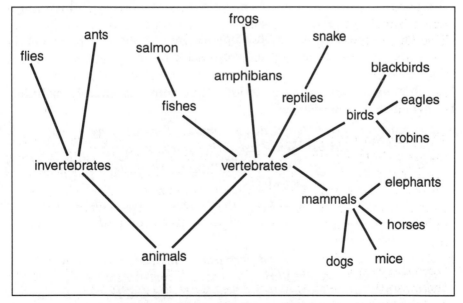

Figure 5.2 Part of a simple tree

and decide whether some led to more useful groupings than others and whether some criteria would allow other animals to be fitted into the groupings. This developed into work about the use of trees to show the relationships between animals:

As well as everyday classroom activities being used as starting points for learning science, many of the objects found in primary classrooms offer numerous possibilities for teaching science. For example, most classrooms have percussion instruments that are used for making music and accompanying singing. Seven year old Christopher had been banging a cymbal with a beater when his teacher asked him to draw a diagram to show how sound travelled from the cymbal to his ear:

the Vibration
the cymbal of music when I banged

Figure 5.3   Seven year old Christopher's drawing showing the sound travelling from the cymbal to his ear

She then asked him some questions that helped him to form links between music and science:

- *You said that cymbals are always made of metal. Why do you think that might be? Would any other material work as well? How could we try to find out? What about their shape? Would another shape work as well?*

- *What do you know about the skin of a drum? What do you think affects the sound a drum makes? How could you make a drum make a high note?*

- *What do you think the word percussion means? In how many different ways can you play a percussion instrument? How do you think the sound is made in each way? Could you try to make a percussion instrument that can be played in at least two different ways?*

Identifying the scientific potential

Approaching science through activities and objects that are readily available provides the children with repeated opportunities to make their own discoveries, to satisfy their curiosity, to construct meanings and to make links with the scientific ideas that they already hold. However, it also means that we as teachers have to identify the scientific potential in the everyday activities and objects in our surroundings that both we and the children already feel confident in using. We can do this by first of all assessing the activity or object in terms of the main science concepts. Does it lend itself to teaching and learning about:

- the characteristics and classification of living and non-living things?
- how living and non-living things can change state, form or position?
- how living and non-living things behave, work and interact with each other?

Many teachers and children enjoy singing the traditional song 'I know an old lady who swallowed a fly'. If we look at this song in terms of the main science concepts we realise that it contains ideas about:

- the characteristics and classification of living things
- how living things can change state
- how living things interact with each other.

Having identified these broad concepts, we can break them down into the smaller scientific concepts that are embedded within them:

- the characteristics of flies, spiders, birds, cats, dogs, goats and horses that enable us to identify them as specific groups of animals
- the classification of flies and spiders into invertebrates (animals with no backbone) and birds, cats, dogs, goats and horses into vertebrates (animals with backbones). The vertebrates can further be sub-divided into birds and mammals and the mammals grouped into herbivores and carnivores.
- how each animal is changed by the process of nutrition into a food that is taken into the body, digested, absorbed and the remains eliminated.
- how the different animals interact with each other by becoming food sources for other animals.

The animals in the song are a fictitious food chain; that is a chain of animals each of which feeds on and obtains energy from the preceding one and in turn is eaten by and provides energy for the following one. A real-life food chain rarely has more than five levels; the one in the song exceeds this. The song also omits the plant that always is the starting point of every food chain, and the bacteria at the end of it that break the dead bodies down into organic materials that are then available as plant nutrients. The size of the animals increases as the song progresses and, as a rule, there are bigger animals at each level in a food chain, but fewer of them, because much of the energy obtained from nutrition is lost in respiration and thus fewer animals can be supported in each succeeding level. This is known as the pyramid of numbers.

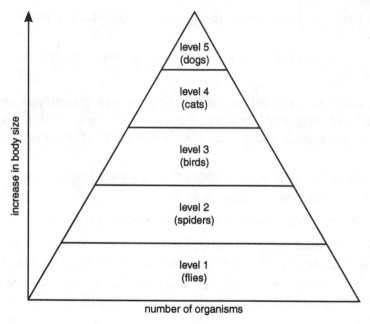

Figure 5.4 Pyramid of numbers

Developing the scientific potential

To develop the scientific potential of the song 'I know an old lady who swallowed a fly' into a teaching opportunity, we next have to decide which science concepts we want to develop further. We will then need to use one or more of the many methods already outlined to find out what the children already know about it. Then we will need to refer to the school science policy, other science texts and the National Curriculum in order to decide what concepts it is appropriate for the children to be working towards next. In doing so, of course, we have to remember that the National Curriculum sets out a minimum entitlement, rather than the science that could be taught, and that we should not be limited by its requirements.

A teacher who had heard about this method of working on an Inset course and wanted to try it out decided to use this song to help her class of eight year olds to develop their understanding of food chains. First, she needed to find out what the children already knew about food chains. Through brainstorming, questioning and discussion, she discovered that most of the children had had little experience of food chains, had few ideas that animals are interdependent in this way and did not realise that energy is transferred from one animal to the next by this means. She then decided that there were a number of science concepts that the children could work towards next, including:

- animals feed in order to obtain the energy necessary to stay alive
- some animals obtain their energy by feeding on plants (herbivores)
- some animals obtain their energy by feeding on plants and animals (omnivores)
- some animals obtain their energy by feeding on other animals (carnivores)
- carnivores obtain their energy by eating herbivores, omnivores or other carnivores
- some carnivores are not eaten by any other animals
- animals are dependent on what they eat. Any animal eating another animal is also indirectly dependent on what *that* animal has eaten, whether it was a plant or yet another animal. This feeding and obtaining energy from other animals or plants links animals together in the food chain.
- the animals at the start of a food chain are usually smaller and more numerous than the animals at the end of the food chain
- food chains are not usually isolated but are cross-linked to form a food web.

Obviously there were too many science concepts for the children to learn about at once, so the teacher selected those that she believed were the most appropriate, useful and necessary ones for the children at that time. She decided to focus on the similarities and differences between carnivores, omnivores and herbivores.

She next considered which science skills and attitudes could also be developed at the same time and decided that it would be appropriate for the children to build on and extend their skills of:

- observing and describing
- using secondary sources
- collecting and looking for patterns in data

in order to develop their attitudes of:

- curiosity
- perseverance
- co-operation.

Developing learning activities

The teacher next looked at published schemes of work to find activities that could form starting points for the children's learning about carnivores, omnivores and herbivores. She searched specifically for activities that could be differentiated to meet the varied needs of different children as she was aware that the same work would not provide adequately for all the children. She also felt it was important to support the children to become independent and self-directing learners, and to encourage them to enjoy discovering and satisfying their curiosity about the world around them. She asked the course organiser for help with this, explaining that "I want the children to have the freedom to choose, so the activities mustn't be too prescriptive and should have possibilities for different ways of being carried out. I want to avoid giving the children the impression that I know what we are going to do and that I have decided the way we are going to do it. I want them to have opportunities to demonstrate creativity and to take some responsibility for their own learning, yet at the same time I want to retain flexibility for myself." The course organiser and teacher drew up the following check-list of points that they felt needed to be considered when choosing activities:

- Are there a number of ways that the activity could develop?
- Does the activity allow the children to make discoveries and raise their curiosity?
- Can the activity be differentiated to meet the needs of the children who are to do it?
- Would the activity stimulate the children to ask questions and want to find out or do more?
- Do we have all the resources the activity requires?
- What criteria will we need to use to decide if the children are learning any scientific concepts, skills or attitudes by carrying out the activity?

As part of this work on food chains the teacher decided that a card sort was a suitable activity for helping some of the children to distinguish between carnivores, omnivores and herbivores. She provided a pile of cards with the name of a different animal written on each one (picture cards could have been used if the children were not able to read the names). Her original idea was that the children would take turns to take a card, decide whether the animal was a carnivore, omnivore or herbivore, and place it on an appropriate pile. At the end of the game the children themselves could check whether or not they had placed each card in the correct pile by using books to look up the animals' diets.

However, the teacher also felt that this activity could develop in different ways, and that her original idea did not have to be the one that the children had to follow. She thought that the cards could also be used to play snap the carnivore, omnivore or herbivore, or as a beat-the-clock team game. However, John and Amy found another way in which to use the cards when they took turns to play a 20 Questions type of game to find out the name of each animal:

Does it eat meat? Yes, but not much.

Does it eat vegetables? Yes.

Is it an omnivore? Yes.

Has it got four legs? No.

Has it got two legs? Yes.

Is it a bird? No.

Is it a mammal? Yes.

Is it a person? No.

Is it hairy all over? Yes.

Is it a monkey? No.

Does it have a tail? No.

Is it an ape? Yes.

Does it live in Africa? Yes.

Is it a chimpanzee? Yes.

The card sort encouraged the children to become curious and to find out more about the exact diet of each animal, how their teeth are adapted to what they eat and some of the other characteristics of the different carnivores, herbivores and omnivores shown on the cards. As it was an activity that stimulated discussion and raised questions about habitats and predators, the children needed access to good reference books.

The teacher had previously decided the criteria that she would use in order to say that the children had learnt about carnivores, herbivores and omnivores. She was satisfied if they could do one or more of the following:

- correctly sort all the animals
- say how they knew each animal was a carnivore, herbivore or omnivore
- correctly check the cards sorted by another child or group
- talk about the precise diet of some of the animals.

As well as developing the children's concepts about the differences between carnivores, herbivores or omnivores, the card sort also enabled them to develop various scientific skills and attitudes. It encouraged the children to use books to find out information about animals' habitats and eating habits; to describe in detail the teeth and diet of the animals; to look for patterns in the information that they collected; to become curious about animals that they did not know much about; to persevere in finding out information and to share that information and co-operate with others.

Wider perspectives for learning science

Although science can be taught through many of the familiar activities and objects in the classroom, it can also be taught through other areas of the curriculum, to help the children strengthen the links between their various learning experiences. This also gives the children practice in transferring their skills and learning from one context to others, and to express their understanding and competencies in different ways. By sometimes taking science outside its normal limits we can give the children a broader view of it, and show its relevance to their lives and to the lives of others nowadays and in the past. Children often find learning science in this way less effort and more fun.

Learning science out of doors

Much geography and environmental education are based on science; and through them science can most easily be made accessible out of doors as well as in the classroom. Most children already have ideas about natural and man-made materials in the environment, different types of environment and the effects that human activities have on them. We can develop the children's awareness of these issues by asking them to plan a nature trail around the school or local neighbourhood. By focusing their attention on the familiar in their surroundings we can encourage children to gain a greater understanding of seasonal changes and the micro-climates that abound in a small area. In order to make their own nature trail the children will need to walk around the area and assess what they think might be of interest to others. They will need to consider factors such as using different senses to identify a variety of features along the trail, the information that it might be useful to provide for those going on the trail (and in what format), the effects that may be caused by a number of people using the trail and how this might be managed, and so on. Once the trail has been devised it will need to be trialled, evaluated and, if necessary, adapted before being shared with others.

Art can also be used as a way of teaching science. Drawing and painting from life, whether a minute specimen or a vast landscape, encourages children to observe closely; and as they do so they can gain a greater understanding of space and scale and the ways in which organisms and parts of organisms relate to each other. The aesthetic side of science can be developed by encouraging the children to see and appreciate beauty in both the natural and the man-made, and to consider ways in which scientific models or artefacts can be made more aesthetically pleasing. The children can contribute to making a more aesthetic environment, by, for example, turning a neglected corner into a more pleasant one. Such a project gives great scope for creativity while involving much science, as the children will have to draw on their scientific knowledge and skills to design and make wall tiles, plan and plant flower beds or pots, think about the use of materials and techniques to make a wind sculpture, and collaborate with others to make their ideas a reality and to maintain the area.

Historical aspects of science can be emphasised by looking at some of the natural changes that have occurred over a long period of time. Children can look at written sources and physical remains to gain an appreciation of their heritage and an understanding of some of the long-term changes that have taken place in, for example, an established hedgerow or wood, or in a comparison of present and past land use. They can look at an old church with an established graveyard, as old buildings provide opportunities for the children to survey a range of building materials and investigate weathering, other wear and tear and a variety of habitats adopted by a range of plants and animals.

Science can also be given a world-wide dimension by considering global issues and the geographical, historical, political and social contexts that may conflict with them. This kind of approach to science can help children realise that it is not value or culture-free, and to question and consider alternative viewpoints in order to understand that there is a difference between opinion and fact. A class of ten year old children had grown food plants and investigated conditions necessary for growth. Different groups then explored traditional farming methods in different parts of the world, the need for soil conservation, the use of and dependency on artificial fertilisers and crop rotation. Many of these issues challenged the children's attitudes, assumptions and stereotypes whilst also encouraging them to become aware of the limitations of science.

Learning science by looking at the past

Both human activity and the natural changes that have occurred over time have shaped the evolution of scientific ideas and methods throughout the history of the world. People have always used science to help them solve problems, and by becoming aware of this the children can begin to appreciate the historical aspect of science. Studying pictures in books or art galleries can show the children what life was like in 'the old days', what different artefacts there were and how they were used and by whom. A visit to a museum to look at artefacts can help children to gain an understanding of what they were like, why they were invented and how they worked.

An inflammable gas known as fire-damp can be found in patches in coal seams. During the Industrial Revolution in Britain miners worked by the light of naked flames and, as coal mines were made bigger and deeper, gas explosions occurred more frequently and hundreds of miners were killed every year. In 1815 Sir Humphry Davy analysed the gas and discovered that it would not explode if it was mixed with air inside a very narrow tube. He was then able to use this knowledge to invent a safety lamp for the miners. He later improved the design of his safety lamp so that the size of the flame increased in the presence of fire-damp, thus warning the miners that fire-damp was in the atmosphere and giving them a chance to seek safety. The Davy lamp revolutionised the lives of miners, and children nowadays can begin to appreciate how important an invention it was by looking at it carefully and considering it from both a historical and a scientific perspective.

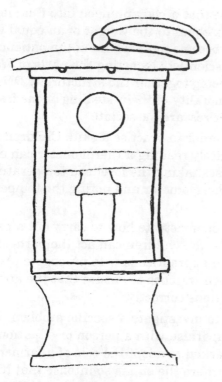

Figure 5.5   Eight year old Katherine's drawing of a Davy lamp

Learning science through drama

Science can be explored through drama and role-play, and both can be developed in a variety of ways to highlight different aspects of science. Its organisation in the classroom will depend on the space and time available, how many children can take part at once, how the audience will be arranged, whether there is to be a script or not, and if so who writes it, and so on. Drama and role-play can be used to help break down some of the stereotypes of gender and culture that may exist. Both require children to have enough information about the subject matter so that they can communicate about it through their words and gestures, and this means that they will also need time in which to prepare their presentation and familiarise themselves with the character they are to play.

- Descriptive drama can be used to enable children to gain a greater understanding of others by acting out the lives of different people. For example, they may become more aware of the difficulties encountered by blind and deaf people and their determination to overcome such difficulties by acting the parts of Helen Keller, her family and teachers. They may become more aware of the excitement felt at a scientific breakthrough by acting the part of Archimedes shouting "Eureka!" when he discovered the principle that a body plunged into fluid loses as much of its weight as is equal to the weight of an equal volume of the fluid. They may become more aware of the patience and persistence needed by scientists by acting the parts of Watson and Crick doggedly piecing together the structure of DNA, and can also consider the morality of their 'stealing' ideas from Rosalyn Franklin, their research associate.

• Drama can be used in order to practise a skill. Children who need practise in accurately reading a thermometer can act in a hospital drama as nurses taking the forehead temperatures of patients with a strip thermometer and noting the temperature on their charts.

• Drama can be used to demonstrate how to carry out a particular technique. For example, the children can act the parts of a gardener who shows an apprentice how to propagate plants by taking cuttings and then watches to ensure that the apprentice carries out the instructions correctly.

• Role-play can be used to investigate a specific problem. Role-play enables children to empathise with a person or situation. For example, they can be asked to adopt the role of a farmer living high up in the Andes where the sun is so intense that his fields of wheat seedlings are in danger of becoming burnt. In order to understand the problem and its implications for the farmer, they will need information about the life style and the country. They will then be able to understand why this problem is worrying and how essential it is to overcome it. At the end of a role-play the children may need to be debriefed so that they come out of the role and do not carry the feelings of the role with them.

• Role-play can be used to raise children's awareness of a situation and the variety of attitudes and values that may be held by others. However, role-play of this type can be emotive and needs sensitive handling. For example, controversial environmental issues such as seal culling, whaling or fox hunting can be examined by children who adopt roles that incorporate political, economic or ethical stances. The children will need to research information about these issues in order to be able to argue clearly and concisely from a particular perspective. For this type of role-play to be successful, the objective must be clearly understood by both those participating and those watching. Thus, children adopting the roles of Greenpeace supporters can explain to those acting as members of the Norwegian government why they are against whaling, and the parliamentarians can explain why it is essential in terms of the economy. Those watching can be encouraged to make up their minds about the issue by being required to vote for or against the continuation of whaling at the end of the play.

- One further type of role-play is a simulation in which the children adopt the roles and actions of people in a situation that actually happened, in order to gain an insight into social decision making. For example, the children can adopt the different roles of various officials and the public who attended an enquiry into the proposal for a new by-pass that was to cause the re-routing of 500 metres of river. Obviously in order to do this the children will need information about who was present and in what capacity, how the case developed and what the outcome of the enquiry was. Newspaper articles often provide this.

Learning science by problem solving

Problems that arise during the everyday work of the classroom may contain a scientific potential that can be exploited and turned into a learning activity that is suitable for some or all of the children in the class. Such problem solving exercises require children to use informed judgement to seek practical solutions. When identifying a need and deciding if it is an appropriate one to pursue, we will have to consider whether or not the problem is one that:

- is interesting and relevant
- is understandable by the children
- can develop the children's science concepts, skills or attitudes
- appeals to both girls and boys
- can be resourced
- is possible for the children to attempt to solve and that there is time in which they can try to do so.

How to ensure that the spider plant in their classroom got sufficient water during the half-term break when no-one was there to water it, was a practical problem that a number of seven year olds tried to decide how to solve:

Kimberley: *Take it away from the window then the sun won't dry it up.*

Natalie: *Put it in a big bowl of water, so's it'll have enough to last.*

Kimberley: *Take it away from the window and put it in a big bowl of water.*

Richard: *That'll make it too wet... let the tap drip on it slowly.*

James: *The tap drips would still be too wet.*

Richard: *So how could we make drips that aren't too wet?*

Natalie: *Drip something else?*

Richard: *Like what?*

Natalie: *Something else what drips... like washing.*

In the end the children decided to take the spider plant away from the window, to suspend a length of wet string between two plastic bottles full of water and to place the spider plant below the string so that the water dripped from the string on to the soil in the flower pot.

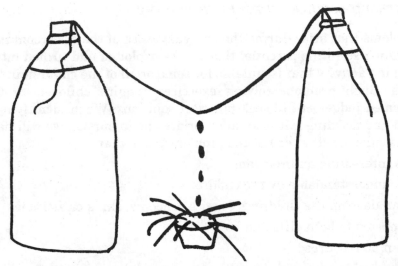

Figure 5.6   Some seven year olds' invention to water a spider plant

Creativity in problem solving can be fostered by deliberately looking at a situation in as many different ways as possible. By becoming more flexible in our thinking, we are able to reflect on the well-established patterns that we have learnt from our previous experiences, and as a result become willing to reconsider and further the concepts that we hold. Our previous ideas may act as stepping stones to other ideas as happened, for example, when in 1690 Papin's attention was arrested by the sight of steam raising the lid of a saucepan of boiling water. He suddenly realised that the steam was acting as a force when it lifted the saucepan lid, and that steam as a force could be made to lift other things in the same way. This led him to devise a piston that was moved by steam, and ultimately in 1712 Thomas Newcomen used Papin's idea as a fundamental part of his steam engine.

We can help children to look for alternative solutions and not simply to be satisfied with their first solution to a problem by persuading them to explore further, and only then evaluate their strategies and solutions. This type of creativity can be fostered by encouraging the children:

- to defer judgement until a number of possible solutions have been suggested rather than evaluating each solution at once
- to meet deadlines and quotas: "You've got five minutes to come up with three ideas."
- to realise that solutions do not have to be logical, rational or conform to the ideas of others
- not to worry about making mistakes, failing or looking foolish.

A group of six year olds was asked to spend five minutes generating as many solutions as possible to the problem of how to make sure that the door to the toilets was kept closed. They noted the following ideas:

- *Put a spring between the door and the door frame, so the spring pulls the door shut.*
- *Put a mirror on the wall opposite the door so you see your face when you come out and put a fluorescent notice like a speech bubble coming out of your face in the mirror saying HAVE YOU SHUT THE DOOR?*
- *Make an alarm so when the door is open it makes a horrible noise and it won't stop till you shut the door.*
- *Take turns at sitting by the door and being in charge of shutting it.*
- *Train Jemma's dog to shut it.* (Jemma's dog was well known to the class as being able to do tricks!)
- *Keep the door locked.*

The children evaluated their ideas at the end of five minutes and concluded that neither keeping the door locked nor training Jemma's dog were viable solutions and that although taking it in turns to sit and shut the door was viable, they did not want to do it. They decided that using a mirror and a speech bubble was the most exciting solution and although they were not sure that it would work, they wanted to develop this solution further. In the end the group decided to use a big sheet of plastic mirror, bend it and fix it to the wall so that it curved like a convex mirror. They thought that other children might take more notice of faces in a curved mirror than a flat one. When they came to fix the mirror to the wall they found that the children's faces were at different heights, but by using two sheets of mirror they were able to position the mirror so that everyone could see themselves. They then fixed a very large and colourful speech bubble at the side of the mirror. Although the children enjoyed pulling faces in the mirror as they came out of the toilet, they did not always remember to shut the door. However, making sure that the door was closed became less of a problem than before.

Summary

Teaching science involves providing children with a variety of experiences and activities that helps them to construct meanings, make links with their previous knowledge, and develop their scientific skills and attitudes. A science education that is as accessible and wide ranging as possible enables children to strengthen the links between their various learning experiences and to understand the relevance of science to their daily lives. Science can take place both inside and outside the classroom using everyday and familiar objects and activities, as well as those that are more unusual and those that at first glance may not be considered as starting points for science. The scientific potential of any object or activity can be gauged by assessing it in terms of the main science concepts that can be taught through it; by deciding which of those concepts are appropriate to the children's learning at that moment; and by considering which scientific skills and attitudes can also be developed. Learning experiences that are relevant to the object or activity can then be devised or chosen from schemes, in order to help the children to develop the appropriate concepts, skills and attitudes. Such learning experiences need to be ones that can be differentiated to meet the varied needs of all the children and also ones that will stimulate and satisfy them.

6 Organising the teaching and learning of science

It is extremely difficult for any teacher to keep from getting into a rut. The continual effort to make things simple and elementary for children is apt to deaden the intellect.

A. S. Neill, *A Dominie's Log*

There is no one 'right' way in which to organise science in the primary classroom. Different ways of organising both the class and the classroom are appropriate for different times and purposes. Often different ways encourage different learning styles, and so using different methods ensures that all the children have a chance to feel at ease with what and how they are learning at some point. Changes made in organisation will inevitably have a knock-on effect. Thus, for example, re-allocating groups enables the children to learn to co-operate with a wider range of people and provides them with opportunities to encounter different working methods, thinking styles and ideas. Particular topics lend themselves to some approaches more than others, and a fresh approach can stimulate a new interest or revive one that is flagging. However, when choosing organisational methods we need to take into account the ethos and aims of the school as a whole, so that we maintain a holistic approach to the children's education.

Organising children for science

When teaching science we need to organise children in ways that:
- are appropriate for different children
- will support their development of the particular concept or skill that we have identified for them to learn or practise
- enable us to establish the ideas that the children are using.

We also need to be realistic in our expectations of what it is possible for each child to achieve, and make sure that our organisation enables this to happen.

In most cases we can effect this by a balance of reading, writing, talking and carrying out practical work and a combination of class work, group work and individual work. This chapter outlines some advantages and disadvantages of a variety of methods for organising the teaching and learning of science.

Class work

There are occasions when we will want science to be a whole class activity. For example, when starting a science topic, it may be appropriate to introduce it to all the children at once; and similarly at the end of a topic we can summarise together the work that has been done. We may also want use class time to give out instructions, or introduce new work or terminology to all the children during a topic, or provide everyone with an opportunity to review on-going work. By using class time to introduce various activities to different groups, we enable all the children to be aware of what is going on in the class as a whole, which they may not be if we introduce activities to groups individually.

Discussion

Discussion provides an opportunity for children to probe and focus their own and others' ideas. It helps children to learn by making links and generalisations for themselves; but in order for them to do so the teacher has to allow `children to make the connections for themselves rather than making them for them. This approach is neither didactic nor directed by the teacher and is not always easy to manage. As only a few children can participate at any one time, a discussion with the whole class will not maintain everyone's interest. It can also be difficult for all children to follow and makes no allowance for their individual needs. The different roles they may adopt can also influence their contribution to a discussion. The quiet child who has adopted the role of dilly-dreamer or flounderer may withdraw and take no interest in the proceedings; whereas the child who has adopted the role of brains or funny-kid may attempt to take over.

Demonstration lesson

Occasionally demonstrating to the whole class is the most effective means of teaching, or an essential prerequisite of it. For example, we may want to show all the children how a new piece of equipment, such as a microscope, works and how best to use it and look after it; or we may need to explain a new technique, such as how to measure the swing of a pendulum; or show the children how to work in a particular way, in order to carry out an activity safely. To demonstrate these to the whole class saves the teacher time, as the same thing does not have to be repeated over and over again to different groups of children. We can carry out such a demonstration ourselves or call upon individual children to do so. Of course, demonstrating science to a whole class of children does not actively involve them or provide them with first hand experience and takes no account of their differing abilities and understanding. We cannot be certain that all the children have paid attention and grasped what is being demonstrated, so to ensure that the demonstration has meaning for each and every child in the class, they will all need to follow it up and try it out for themselves, as until they do so they will not have had the opportunity to learn with understanding.

Group work

Putting children into groups when learning science enables individuals to encounter different perspectives about the same idea and to realise that there may be alternatives to their way of thinking. Group work requires the children to be more effective in their learning, as they are expected to interact with each other in order to communicate their ideas, and listen to and reflect on those of others. This means that for grouping to contribute to teaching and learning it has to be more than a convenient seating arrangement. Learning in groups is a more complex and demanding activity than whole class learning and cannot function effectively in a classroom unless the children are able to respect their own and each others' learning and to use listening and negotiating skills.

The size, composition and arrangement of the groups all have a marked bearing on how well they function, and the children's adoption of roles (goody-goody, nice-kid and so on) will influence decisions about who sits with whom. The sex, race and maybe even religion of group members needs to be considered at all times but particularly when groups are discussing sensitive or emotional issues, as children who come from groups that feel differently about particular issues may feel inhibited and have little motivation to join in discussions. A solitary girl in a group of boys may be discouraged from asking questions and contributing her ideas to a discussion about the human life cycle. Similarly, a child who is of a different race from other members of a group may well feel differently and prefer not to discuss the observable similarities and differences between group members.

Children as a group can be given activities that meet their learning needs, as well as providing them with a purpose for interaction and encouraging them to develop their skills, attitudes and use of scientific language. A mixed group of eight year olds needed opportunities to stimulate their creativity and to further their ideas about the ways in which forces act on an object. To encourage these their teacher asked them to design a game that used a rubber band to propel a ball across a floor. The children initially discussed the ideas that they already held about forces. All the children knew that forces make things start, stop, speed up or slow down; some children knew that they acted in opposite directions; others knew that friction was a force. They then considered rubber bands: their length and thickness, the relationship between the amount they can be pulled back and the distance a ball will travel, and so on. They made decisions about the method of playing their game, the rules, scoring, etc. before designing a game, trying out their ideas, modifying them and making a prototype. In order to do all this, the group had to understand its task and share commitments to respect all group members ideas and collectively to decide the way in which the task was to be carried out. All the children had a purpose for interacting as well as opportunities to express their own ideas, hear those of others and affirm or modify their understanding of forces acting on an object.

Grouping children for learning science

Traditionally children in primary classrooms are grouped according to various criteria, such as ability in a given subject, stage of working, those who work well together and those who must be kept apart at all costs. If the teaching of science is a way of doing, seeing and thinking, based on the children's experiences and the concepts that they hold, then our grouping of children for learning science should reflect this. We also need to match the requirements of the children to the science activities that we give them, or provide activities that the children themselves can interpret in their own ways to meet their needs, rather than provide the same work for all the children regardless of their needs and ideas. This means that we cannot rely exclusively on those published schemes of work that do not provide a range of activities from which we can choose those that best match the needs and ideas of our children. Activities will need to be differentiated or differentiable to meet the varied needs of all children and not only those who find science harder, or need extra support due to any learning difficulties but also those who are exceptionally able at science and who need greater challenges. As an HMI noted[1]:

> The hierarchical nature of most scientific knowledge creates a requirement for teachers to ensure that, as far as is reasonable, new learning builds on the existing knowledge of the pupils. Pupils' progress is too often hindered by poor matching of tasks to needs. The tendency to provide the same work for all pupils in mixed ability classes leads to a significant amount of under-achievement in Key Stages 2, 3 and 4.

When planning to group the children for learning science, we first need to ascertain the range of ideas held by the class, and then make decisions about which science concepts we think are appropriate ones for the children to work towards next and the activities that they will carry out to do so. Researchers at the University of Strathclyde[2] used three specific science tasks to determine the ideas held by 120 eight to twelve year olds about floating in tap water, floating in fluids of different densities and motion down an inclined plane. The children were put into two distinct groups depending on the ideas that they held. In one group the children all held similar ideas and in the other group the children all held different ideas. The children were then asked individually to make and write down predictions about a science task that they were to carry out. Writing down the predictions meant that individual children could not change their minds and could be identified with a specific prediction. Then the groups were asked to compare their predictions. This proved an excellent incentive for lively discussion. From their evidence, the researchers suggested that the interaction between children who held differing scientific concepts was a more effective catalyst for the development of their ideas than the interaction between children who held similar scientific concepts.

This research has implications for the science learning of the children in our classes and, as a result, our classroom organisation.

As it appears that science learning is more effective when there is a range of alternative ideas in a group, we will need to:

i   find out the ideas held by the children

ii decide which science concepts it is appropriate for them to work towards next

iii differentiate activities to meet the children's needs or provide activities that are differentiable by the children

iv organise the children into groups where they hold different ideas, but are working towards the same concept through carrying out appropriate activities.

A teacher of five year olds tried this way of working when she introduced the concept of life processes to her class. She first found out what ideas the children held about this by asking them to draw a picture of something that was alive and to say why they thought that it was alive. Most children drew a mammal although Scott drew a car. When asked why it was alive he replied that it could move. Some other children gave movement as a reason for being alive, others gave breathing, being able to see and one said having babies. No child gave more than one reason. The teacher then decided that the children should first work on their understanding of the differences between living and non-living things. She looked through schemes for activities that would allow the children to interpret them in ways that would meet their needs. By providing activities that were differentiable all the children were able to engage with them at their own level and the teacher was able to look at the outcomes to inform her judgement. She organised the children into groups of three and made sure that in each group she put one child who had given movement as a reason for being alive, one who had given breathing and one who held a different idea.

One activity that she used to help the children to develop the concept of living and non-living was to give each group a pile of cards with pictures of animate and inanimate objects on them. She asked the children to take turns to take a card, to decide whether it was alive or not and to say why they thought so. She did not tell the children how to do this, but left the groups to interpret the activity in their own ways. One group laid all the cards out, took turns to choose a card and say whether it was alive or not and why. The children first chose those cards about which they felt confident, but this left some cards at the end that none of the children really wanted to choose. As the three children held a range of ideas about why things were alive, they were able to draw on each others' ideas and discuss why these last objects might or might not be alive before making a collective decision about categorising them. This raised these children's awareness that there is more than one reason why something is alive. Their teacher felt that they needed further practice to develop this idea, and so she arranged for a parent to bring a dog in, asked the children to look at the dog and ask the parent questions in order to make a list of as many reasons as they could about why the dog was alive.

Another group took turns to sort their cards by asking questions that had 'yes' or 'no' for an answer:

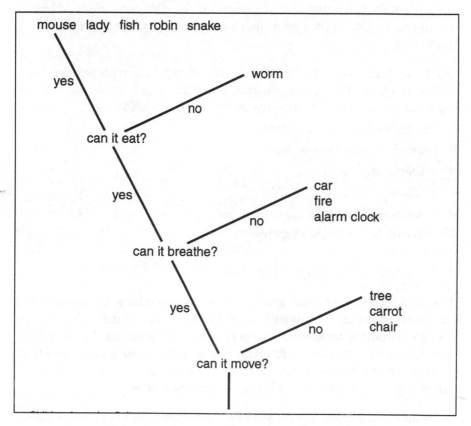

Figure 6.1   A card sort carried out by three five year olds

This caused a lot of discussion, as they first had to agree that by 'move' they meant 'move by itself' and not by an external factor (such as the wind) moving it. They then drew on each others' ideas to discuss whether or not the objects could move, breathe and eat. They eventually concluded that the things that were alive could move, breathe and eat and things that were not alive could not do all three. As the children did not realise that the worm could also eat, their teacher decided that these children would benefit by keeping and observing some worms in a wormery for a while and by studying a range of mini beasts, so that they could broaden their ideas about life processes.

By putting the children into groups with different ideas, and expecting them to use those ideas in carrying out this work, and providing activities that were differentiable, the teacher had to be prepared for the children to work in ways other than any she may have considered. The two groups mentioned had carried out the same card sorting activity but in different ways. However, each had engaged with the activity and drawn on the different ideas of group members, while testing and developing their concept of living and non-living.

Once we have put the children into groups in which they hold different ideas, there are various ways in which it is possible to organise group work for science in the classroom, including:

1 one science group at a time

2 several science groups at once

3 a theme approach

4 a science circus

5 science assignments

6 independent science enquiry.

1 One science group at a time

Teaching science to one group at a time enables us to provide activities that can be tailored to meet the needs of different groups and to introduce new work to each group as required. We can help the children to develop different science concepts in a sequence that is appropriate to them, as we can provide activities that can take place one after another and build on previous ones.

A teacher of a group of nine year olds who held different ideas about forces felt that they needed to develop the concept of forces acting in particular directions. She asked the children to find a way in which to raise a heavy load from A to B. The children had had different experiences of this and their teacher was able to help them to draw on their experiences to discuss and suggest how the activity might be carried out. They then planned the way that they thought was the most appropriate for moving the load, carried out the activity, discussed their results, drew conclusions from them and then talked with their teacher about the forces they had used and the way in which those forces had acted. As she talked to the children the teacher decided that they needed to use the idea that forces act in particular directions in another context, so she suggested that next time they looked at the forces involved in riding a bicycle.

When we have only one group involved in a science activity at any one time, we can arrange to spend time interacting with that group, listening to their ideas and watching what they do and how they work together. We can assign each group a convenient time in which to carry out its science task or investigation. This could be at different times of the day or week to fit in with other activities. The groups can then work at their own pace within the time allocated.

Having only one group involved in a science activity at a time is economical on resources as it requires only one set of equipment to be available at any one time. If necessary an area of the classroom can be set aside as a temporary science area for a while. For example, when the children are carrying out investigations into light, a corner of the classroom can be blacked out on a temporary basis or a dark stock cupboard made available. However, it may be disadvantageous to have an area of the classroom set aside for science for the period of time necessary for all the groups to complete their different activities using it.

This method of organisation enables each group of children to have first hand experience of science, although whether or not each child in the group is directly involved will depend on the group dynamics and the way in which the teacher expects the group to work together. If the group is working effectively the children will have opportunities to develop their communication skills and their attitudes of co-operation, self-discipline and tolerance of others. The children can record their individual contributions to the activity, consider what they have learnt from it and reflect on their performance. The teacher is able to record the experience and achievements of each child and note the progress that they have each made in their scientific understanding, skills and attitudes.

This method can be advantageously adapted for carrying out large scale surveys. The activity is introduced to the class as a whole and the children given time to express their ideas and then discuss and use them to plan in detail how the survey is to be carried out. Successive groups of children then carry out the same activity in the same way. In this way, a larger amount of data will be generated than any one group could reasonably be expected to produce on its own. The data from the different groups is then pooled before analysis. The class as a whole should then have an opportunity to consider the reliability of the results, given that they were obtained by different groups.

2 *Several science groups at once*

In multiple group organisation, a number of different groups are all given their science tasks or investigations to complete at the same time. Although it can be hard for the teacher to manage, there will be occasions when it is desirable for several groups, or even all the groups in the class, to be involved in science activities simultaneously. For example, if the class is investigating different aspects of the growth of seeds, one of the control variables may be the time at which the seeds are sown, in which case all the children would need to sow their seeds at the same time so that direct comparisons could be drawn and any further investigations reasonably be considered as 'fair tests'. As all the children have taken part in these investigations, they will all have the opportunity to be involved in and contribute to report-back sessions. Report-back sessions allow children to develop their communication skills as they compare what the different groups have done, the results obtained and the conclusions drawn.

Activities can be designed to meet the needs of different groups and organised so that the groups work on science concepts in an appropriate sequence. Each group is able to work at its own pace, and science can be arranged to fit in with other activities. However, with a number of groups involved in science at the same time, enough equipment has to be available for each group to use, and this can pose problems. It might be possible to borrow equipment from other classes, science centres or a local secondary school, but as this requires the fetching and returning of equipment it can cause complications.

Obviously, with a number of groups involved in science at the same time, the teacher cannot spend much time interacting with the different groups and may end up as a director of operations rather than a facilitator of learning. Although the teacher can record that all the children have had experience of science, with a number of groups working simultaneously it may be hard to record the precise experience, achievement or progress of each child. However, this can provide an opportunity for the children to take some responsibility for recording. We can encourage them to record their individual contributions to the activity, to reflect on their performance and to consider what evidence (if any) they have to show any progress that they feel they have made with their scientific understanding, skills and attitudes.

3 Theme approach

A theme approach encourages the children to take some responsibility for deciding the subject matter to be learnt. Capitalising on the children's interests in this way can encourage them to be more creative in their approach to science. Themes will need to be chosen with care in order to allow for the progressive development of key scientific ideas. The class as a whole, with the guidance of their teacher, choose a number of areas that they would like to explore on a science theme. At the start of a topic on machines, a teacher of a class of nine year olds wrote "What do we want to find out about machines?" on a large sheet of paper and asked the children to jot down any suggestions that they had. There were too many suggestions to act on in the time available, and so together they narrowed it down to finding out more about levers, cams, gears and drive belts and using them to make some machines of their own. Their teacher had first to find out the ideas that the children already held about levers, cams, gears and drive belts. They were then put into four groups; one group to find out about levers, one to find out about cams, one for gears and one for drive belts. Each group contained children who held different ideas about their subject. The teacher then looked through schemes to find activities that challenged and supported the children's learning about levers, cams, gears and drive belts and would allow the children to differentiate them in ways that they found appropriate to their needs and interests.

As each group's science activity can be organised at different times of the day or week to fit in with other work, multiple sets of resources are not usually needed. However, allowing the children some choice of subject matter increases the possibility that equipment that is not readily available will be required and activities may have to be rethought or carried out at a later date, when the necessary resources have been obtained.

All the children have first hand experience of science as the groups are able to draw on the ideas of their individual members in the planning and carrying out of an activity in an area that they have chosen. The different groups are each able to work at their own pace. This means that the children are able to pursue the tasks or investigations that they have planned in depth and if they decide that a follow-up activity is necessary, or that they want to repeat a part of the task or investigation in order to make changes in their procedure or to check or collect more results, then they can do so without causing difficulties for other groups.

The children also develop their communication skills when reporting their findings and conclusions to the remainder of the class. Each of the groups reporting on levers, cams, gears and drive belts were reporting on something that children in other groups had not experienced. They had to be clear and concise in explaining what they had done and describing their results and findings. Other members of the class were encouraged to listen carefully and ask questions in order to clarify their understanding. The children listening were interested to find out what happened, as they had some responsibility for deciding the subject matter in the first place.

As an alternative to a report-back session, groups can sometimes be asked to write step-by-step instructions to explain how to carry out a particular activity. Other groups can then check the accuracy of these instructions and compare their results with those of the original group. Following others' instructions gives the children opportunities to use methods that they may not have come across before. This is also a useful way to provide groups with practice in developing or refining a particular skill. A group of six year olds who had investigated the thermal insulation properties of a range of fabrics had used a stopwatch to time regular intervals at which to take temperature readings. Their teacher decided that others in the class needed further practice in using a stopwatch and reading a thermometer and suggested that certain children follow the original group's instructions.

As only one group need be involved in science at once, the teacher can arrange to spend time interacting with that group, listening to their ideas, and watching what they do and how they work together. As the children are exploring a different aspect of the theme their experiences as well as their achievements and progress in their scientific understanding, skills and attitudes will be varied, so it will be necessary to keep a careful record of each group's activities. The children can also be encouraged to think about and record their own contribution, performance and learning.

4 Science circus

A circus is simply a variation on the theme approach and one in which the children in a class have the opportunity to experience all (not just one) of the activities. The class, with their teacher, collectively decide on a number of activities that they would like to carry out in a particular area. As this allows the children to have greater ownership of the activities, they are often more interested and motivated in carrying them out. It can be difficult to make the activities chosen sequential or to differentiate them to any degree, so this method of organisation is most useful when there are a number of aspects relating to a particular topic or skill that all the children need to develop. When, for example, the children are finding out about keeping healthy, they may decide to investigate different aspects of diet and exercise by means of activities such as tallying the different types of foods they eat, identifying food values from tin labels, taking pulse rates during different activities, carrying out a survey of the different types of exercise taken by different classes, and finding out how many calories different types of exercise use. All the children can carry out all of these activities, but the order in which they carry them out is probably not important. A circus is not an appropriate method to use if the results of one investigation are necessary for the planning of the next one, as the order in which they are carried out would then be crucial.

Each group of children uses its own ideas to plan and carry out each activity in turn. This means that individual groups may plan and carry out the tasks or investigations in different ways, so their experiences of the activities will be different in detail, although similar overall. Every group will have completed each activity and so all the children are able to share in class discussions and to develop their communication skills. As they will be reporting on something that other children have experienced, albeit in a different way, the children will need to listen carefully in order to compare what they have done with what has been done by other groups. Experience of each activity enables all the children to compare the methods that they have used and the results that they have obtained. This gives the children an opportunity to reflect on the validity of a range of methods and the reliability of their differing results. They can then begin to appreciate that whilst there is not necessarily one 'correct' method, some methods are more valid than others and produce results that are more reliable.

As there are a number of activities for the children to work through, it can take a long time for all of them to complete one science circus if only one or two groups are involved at once, and enthusiasm for the various tasks and investigations may diminish with the passing of time. Therefore, to maintain interest and speed things up, it may be more convenient to set up a circus so that all the children are carrying out science activities at the same time, with groups rotating through the various tasks or investigations in turn. This requires enough equipment to be available for all the children to use at any one time. It also requires the different activities to take approximately the same length of time and the groups to work at roughly the same pace. As this does not always happen, it is advisable to have one more task or investigation than there are numbers of groups, so that any group finishing ahead of others can continue with the 'spare' activity rather than make another group rush to finish. If the whole class is involved in science at the same time, it will be difficult for the teacher to manage to interact at any length with the different groups in order to monitor and facilitate their learning.

This method enables all the children to have first hand experience of science and the chance to develop a creative approach as they work through a range of activities. Each group will have the opportunity to draw on individual members' experiences, ideas and skills in the planning and carrying out of every activity. The children can be encouraged to think about each person's contribution to the group in order to ensure that they do not always contribute to every activity in the same way: fetching equipment, writing up results, etc. Awareness of this can be raised by the group collectively recording individual contributions to the different tasks and investigations.

The teacher will be able to record that all the children have had experience of a number of science activities. However, with all the groups working simultaneously, it will be difficult to record the precise experience, achievement or progress of each child, especially as each group may have planned and carried out each activity in a different way. The children can be given the opportunity to take some responsibility for recording their own learning by noting how they consider they have performed and what they feel that they have achieved or learnt.

5 Science assignments

This method enables the children to begin to take responsibility for the way in which they use their time by giving each group a separate science task or investigation and allowing them to decide for themselves when they will fit it in with their other work. The activities can be differentiated to meet the needs of different groups, and new work can be introduced as and when each group is ready for it. As part of a topic on materials, a teacher decided that one group in her class of ten year olds needed more experience of working with solids and liquids. On Monday morning she set the group an assignment that involved investigating a range of soluble and insoluble solids and told the children that the work was to be finished by Friday lunchtime. The children had to look at the timetable and agree when they would carry out this work, given the other demands on their time.

By giving the groups their assignments at the beginning of the week and requiring them to complete them before Friday afternoon, the children can be encouraged to organise their own learning to some extent, and to take responsibility for the way in which they spend their time. This means that the resources have to be available at all times, so that having decided to carry out their assignment at a particular time they are not prevented from doing so by others using the equipment. A simple booking procedure can be instituted to overcome this problem if necessary. Booking also ensures that only one group is involved in science at once, so that the teacher can be available to spend time interacting with that group.

Planning their own use of time as well as the way in which they carry out the assignment invariably motivates the children as well as developing group co-operation and communication skills. Each group can work at its own pace, and all the children have first hand experience of science. The children can be encouraged to think about and record their own contribution, performance and learning within the group and to reflect on how the decision of when to carry out the activity is reached. The group of ten year olds who were working with solids and liquids were used to science assignments and planning the way in which they used their time. Although they all looked at the timetable together and discussed the week's activities and how long they thought the assignment was likely to take, they took it in turns to decide when each assignment would be carried out.

Careful record keeping is essential in order to chart each child's contribution to the assignment and to monitor their experiences, achievements and progress in their scientific understanding, skills and attitudes. Assignments can be planned to allow sequential development of the children's science concepts and skills. The children are able to pursue a science activity in depth, which gives them the opportunity to repeat a part of their task or investigation in order to check or collect more results or to make changes in their procedure. A group of seven year olds had been given an assignment to investigate the difference in friction between different materials. They drew on their different ideas and then planned to do this by giving a toy car a push, letting it go and finding out how far it travelled across different materials placed on the floor before it came to rest. Once they started their investigation they realised that although they had thought about making sure the test was 'fair' by using the same car, they were not able to control the amount of push

to the car in a fair way. They therefore decided to change the
which they were carrying out the investigation and instead of
g the car, let it go at the top of a ramp that they covered with
ferent materials. They also put the materials on the floor at
tne end of the ramp and measured the distance that the car rolled
across the materials on the floor before coming to a standstill. They
felt that by changing their investigation in this way the results that
they obtained were more accurate and reliable. They also decided
that they wanted to follow up this activity and to try to find out if the
material that they had concluded enabled the car to travel with the
least friction would allow other things to travel with minimum
friction too. They suggested that this could form their next
assignment. When each group is working on its own assignment,
extension activities of this kind can be given to separate groups
without causing organisational problems for other groups. However,
this method does not always make it easy for the children to share
with others what they have done and found out. We need to be aware
that during report-back sessions some children's interest may not be
maintained by listening to accounts of activities that they have not
experienced.

6 Independent science enquiry

An independent science enquiry enables groups to select their own
areas for study and plan their own activities in consultation with the
teacher, irrespective of the science that other groups are doing. The
groups may need guidance in choosing an area for study that builds
on their previous experiences, and in selecting activities that will
support their learning in the chosen area. Encouraging children to
pursue an in-depth enquiry helps them to develop individual and
group study habits, while capitalising on their innate motivation.

A group of five year olds who were fascinated by pirates wanted to
learn about the ways in which sounds could be amplified, as they
were concerned that in the heat of battle pirates may not be able to
hear commands! As this was a real problem from their point of view,
these young children put a great deal of energy into first finding out
that sounds are made by objects as they vibrate, and then that the
vibrations can be damped or increased as a result of which the sound
became quieter or louder. At an age when they would not normally
have learnt about amplitude, they came to understand that the
loudness of the sound was linked to the amplitude of the vibration
causing it. When playing pirates they were able to use this
knowledge to amplify their commands so that they were loud enough
to be heard across the hurly-burly of the playground.

An independent science enquiry is a useful means of providing extension and enrichment activities for those groups that always work fastest or for those who are exceptionally able at science and who need greater challenges. It can also be used by the entire class once the science work required by the National Curriculum, school science policy or other syllabus has been finished, in order to broaden the children's experiences. It can be organised at different times of the day or week for each group to fit in with other work. The children all have first hand experience of science and each group can work at its own pace without pressure from other groups.

Setting time limits that both the children and teacher agree on for carrying out the enquiry and reporting on it can be useful. Limiting the time for report-back sessions can help to prevent children who become so enthusiastic about their own experiences going on at great length and boring others. It can also help when some groups' enquiries so interest the other children that the entire class end up wanting to become involved with combustion, acidity, electromagnetism, or whatever. An agreed time limit can help children realise that there is insufficient time (and possibly resources) available for them all to get involved.

This method of organisation can be very demanding on the teacher, as a wide range of challenging activities, equipment and reference books may be required. Although the areas of study selected may well not allow for the sequential development of science concepts and skills, pursuing an in-depth enquiry develops conditions for autonomous learning. To monitor the progress that they make in their areas of study the teacher will have to spend time interacting with each group as they carry out their science enquiry so that she can listen to their ideas, and watch what they do and how they work together in order to record each child's experience and achievements.

Individual work

All children need the opportunity from time to time to work on their own when carrying out practical science tasks as well as writing and reading activities in science. Individual work enables children to pursue an interest in depth, enjoy finding out and making discoveries for themselves, and practise a range of study skills; and allows them time to become familiar with and competent in using special scientific equipment and vocabulary. It also helps the children to become self-confident and gain attitudes such as self-discipline and perseverance.

When planning science work for individuals, we first have to find out the ideas that they already hold so that we can provide them with challenging experiences that help them to achieve and make progress in the specific concepts, skills and attitudes that we hope that they will learn or practise. Individual science work can be given to each child in order to meet a specific need, or the teacher and child can negotiate the work to enable the child to follow a particular interest. The activities chosen to support the child's learning can be differentiated and arranged in a sequence that will aid the development of his scientific ideas and skills. New work can be introduced at the rate that he requires and can be repeated in a number of different contexts that are appropriate to him. By repeating science skills and concepts in different contexts, rather than once in only one context, the child is more likely to make links and learn with understanding. A child also needs time on his own in order to reappraise what he knows. This may involve talking things through to himself out loud so that he can clarify his ideas and give up any previously held ones that have now become untenable.

Sometimes we may need to differentiate work or give extra support in order to help individual children to fulfil their potential. Some children may need individual help because they have a learning difficulty of some sort, or are exceptionally able, or have a physical or sensory difficulty. For some children it may be a question of getting the balance of activity (reading, writing, and practical work) or context right so as to enable them not only to take part in science, but to give them an opportunity to be successful in doing so. This may mean that we may have to adapt resources specifically for some children to use. For example, a partially sighted child may require text to be written in a simple, bold style or dictated onto a tape that he can play on a tape recorder.

Other points to consider

Science area

Space in the classroom is always limited, and the space that there is needs to be utilised in such a way that different activities can occur with minimum disruption. Some teachers like to set aside areas of the classroom for particular activities, including a permanent science area, as this enables resources to be located where they are likely to be used. A science co-ordinator and teacher together drew up the following list of points that they felt needed considering when setting up a science area in the teacher's classroom:

- the arrangement of furniture (tables, book shelves, display boards, etc.)
- the storage of resources
- the seating of children (visibilty, access to other requirements e.g. sink, etc.)
- whether or not all resources were to be accessible to all children at all times
- whether or not the children were able to use the resources independently of adult supervision
- whether or not the children should choose for themselves the items that they wanted to use
- whether or not it would be more appropriate for some resources to be kept under the teacher's control
- the appropriateness of the resources for the children and their suitability as to purpose
- labelling and safety issues (especially if any items were stored in containers that were not their original ones)
- disposal of used items and arrangements for their replacement
- checking of items that wear out over a period of time (batteries, light bulbs, etc.)
- regular maintenance of equipment.

Race and culture

Racial and cultural issues can affect the teaching and learning of science in the primary classroom. Nowadays most schools and teachers are aware of and avoid blatant discrimination and obviously biased materials. However, we may sometimes unconsciously adopt a narrow, male, Western view of school science and as a result we may disadvantage some children by the content or context in which we set our science teaching.

We can raise awareness of racial and cultural issues by:
- setting the teaching and learning of science in as diverse a human, social, cultural and environmental context as possible
- avoiding making stereotypical judgements and assumptions based on race or culture
- helping children to understand racial differences in terms of evolution, variation, natural selection and adaption to environment
- challenging any ideas that devalue groups of people on the basis of their skin colour

- refuting any false genetic principles that may be used to support racism (the concept of human race has no genetic validity and it is inappropriate to define racial types by their observable physical differences).

Science is not a new discipline, but children may not appreciate that scientific ideas and methods have evolved throughout the history of the world. We can help children to become aware of the historical and geographic aspects of science by setting it within a technological context and pointing out that different technologies have been, and still are, appropriate and relevant to different cultures at different times. This is most easily done by choosing materials and illustrations that reflect positive images of peoples and cultures and are drawn from many societies to show how local peoples, both nowadays and in the past, make use of science and technology in dealing with their indigenous problems. We need to ensure that we choose examples of non-Western science from a wide range of environments from all parts of the world, and not only from developing countries, so that stereotypes of the Third World are not reinforced. Indeed, the term 'Third World' is contentious in itself, implying a negative and undeveloped status. This means that we may need to check the suitability of library books and other reference materials, as many older publications only mention the 'Third World' in relation to malnutrition, starvation and disease.

It may be necessary to arrange in-class support for children whose language or dialect inhibits or even prevents their learning of science. We may also need to support children from some cultures and life styles where they have been used to being 'seen rather than heard'. We may have to challenge such undervaluing, and encourage children to draw on their rich and varied backgrounds, to share their experiences, to realise that their ideas and experiences are of interest and value to others, and to help them to develop their self-esteem.

Gender

The image of science as remote, abstract, somehow separate from the 'real' world and something that 'men do' is one that many children have already acquired by the time they start school. The masculine image is one that may have been reinforced by the play activities that children are often given at home. Boys more than girls tend to be given battery-operated toys, models to make and things that they can take apart. These kinds of activities provide boys with a wider range of scientific experiences and more opportunities than girls to develop spatial awareness, gain confidence in handling equipment and acquire an innate understanding of some scientific principles, as a result of which the masculine image of science is further augmented. Many adults also assume that all boys will have had these kinds of play experiences and so they sometimes incorrectly infer that all boys can 'do' science and that if they do not 'do' science it is because they have chosen not to and not because they are unable to do it.

Gender differentiation and consolidation at an early age undoubtedly contribute to many girls' lack of interest in science, their perception of it as not being relevant to their lives, and their impersonal approach to it. This can result in some girls behaving hesitantly in practical science tasks, discussions and the way in which they answer questions. Unfortunately this reticence on the part of girls can cause boys to assume (incorrectly) that, as far as science goes, girls are stupid and do not know the answer. This assumption may be given further credence if the girls have adopted the role of flounderer or dilly-dreamer. One way of helping girls who are hesitant to become more involved and confident is to give them the opportunity to work together as pairs and in single sex groups rather than mixed pairs or groups.

For girls to become interested and active participants in learning science, it needs to be taught in ways that reduce its masculine image, and set within a context that girls appreciate as being both useful and important. Various initiatives, such as the 'Girls into Science and Technology Project' and 'Women into Science and Engineering', have suggested that science could be made more girl-friendly by strategies such as:

- helping children to find out about the possible uses and applications of the key scientific ideas involved in the tasks and activities that they undertake: for example, we can help children to realise that weight is a force by sitting a child on the raised end of a see-saw and asking them to explain what will happen if we let go when no-one is sitting on the lower end. The children can then be encouraged to think about how they use weight as a force when levering a lid off a tin.

- linking physical scientific principles to the human body: for example, helping the children to realise that the lens in a simple camera focuses light in the same way that the lens in the eye does.

- discussing scientific issues so as to provide a balanced view of the advantages and disadvantages of scientific developments

- making displays of physical science materials as aesthetically appealing as biological ones. (Any text or picture of science activities should show females as equally as involved and able as males.)
- using imaginative writing as an aid to assimilating scientific principles and ideas.

Changes,

Blackening, destroying,

Smoky, smelly, dirty,

Gobbled up by flames,

Forever.

Figure 6.2 Eight year old Pat's cinquaine about the irreversible nature of burning

When we are considering the context in which to set a science topic, we need to choose one that does not unduly reflect a male orientation. To help children to appreciate the relevance of science we also need to choose a context that emphasises that science is a part of everyday life. When planning to teach a topic on forces a teacher of eight year olds decided to introduce it through sailing. She borrowed a dinghy sail and rigged it up in her classroom so that the children could raise and lower it by means of a pulley. This provided both girls and boys with the opportunity to express their ideas about balanced and unbalanced forces, to suggest ways in which they could measure the force needed to raise the sail, and to wonder what difference it would make to use other types and sizes of pulleys, thus setting up possibilities for investigations to answer the questions that the children had raised.

We can also help the children to focus on the social and economic implications of science through activities such as:

- writing letters (letters can be sent to a local shops asking what their policy is on the packaging of goods).
- reading, or being read, newspaper accounts (different accounts of an oil spillage from a tanker can provide information about the effects on the environment and people's lives, and the cost of the disaster).

- interviewing people (a range of views can be gained about the siting of wind farms).
- keeping a class diary (children can monitor the progress of a local environmental issue).
- collecting and studying magazine advertisements (advertisements for pesticides can be collected and children can discuss the pros and cons of chemical versus biological control).
- looking at information provided to consumers (children can look at heating bills and consider ways in which fuel could be saved).
- recycling goods. Five year old Oliver explained:

I collect egg boxes from the houses round us. I take them to the man in the health food shop. It saves him buying new ones. He gives me an aniseed ball for every egg box.

Safety

Whatever method of teaching science is adopted, we also need to consider the safety issues peculiar to science. Most dangers that the children come across in science are no greater than those they are likely to experience in their daily lives. Most dangers can be anticipated through:

- mentally running through or even trying out activities which are unfamiliar, in order to assess the amount of danger involved and decide on appropriate safety precautions
- stressing the safety precautions rather than dangers
- ensuring that every activity is appropriate for the children who are to carry it out and within their manipulative skills
- checking (with parents if necessary) that the children are physically fit for any strenuous activities that they are to do
- limiting movement around the classroom to a minimum and insisting that care is taken, particularly when the children are carrying heavy or awkward things, dropping things from a height or testing materials to breaking point
- clearly labelling any materials that are put into containers other than their original ones. Any labels should mean something to the children using them. The children can be given a matching game to help them to recognise the various international warning signs that denote the contents of containers (figure 6.3)
- disposing of substances in ways that are appropriate to them
- knowing how to get help in the unlikely event of an accident or other emergency (a knowledge of first aid is useful in this respect)

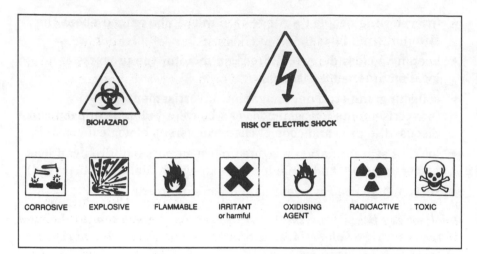

Figure 6.3 International warning signs

- checking sites for field work and visits in advance, so that you are aware of any particular dangers that may be associated with them. Exposure may become a problem if the weather changes unexpectedly and the children do not have enough of the right clothing with them. Small children have a surface area to volume ratio that is much larger than an adult's and their capacity to lose heat is thus correspondingly greater. Even if the teacher is not cold, a small child may be

- checking for specific guidance on safety in LEA guidelines, CLEAPSS guides and the ASE booklet *Be safe!*[3].

Physical harm

Science in the primary classroom is unlikely to harm children physically, particularly if the teacher and children can agree and abide by 'rules' that help to minimise any dangers. A teacher and her class of seven year olds agreed that:

- everyone should be suitably clothed for the activity that they are undertaking, which may mean that their clothes and hair have to be tied back out of the way or protective clothing (including goggles) donned.

- nobody should eat or drink whilst carrying out a science activity. Objects should not be put into noses, ears or mouths unless the teacher has specifically said that they can be. If possible disposable objects should be used but, if objects have to be shared between children, they should be sterilised between use.

- everyone should wash their hands at the end of any science activity involving the use of chemicals or soil of any kind.
- nobody should make very loud sounds near people's ears or look at the sun through a lens, as this could cause permanent damage.
- it is not telling tales to let the teacher know that an accident has occurred.

Mental harm

Although emphasis is usually placed on ensuring that children are not harmed physically, mental dangers are inherent in some science topics, and so we need to be alert to this possibility when planning and supervising science activities. Areas that may need sensitive handling include:

- Being careful that physical characteristics that fall at either end of a range are not unduly emphasised by either the teacher or other children, as this may cause anguish to the child concerned. This situation may arise with topics such as 'Ourselves', when, for example, the children may suggest taking measurements of weight or girth to the chagrin of those children who are the heaviest or fattest. Other sensitive areas include skin colour, wearing an eye patch or glasses, physical abnormalities or deformities, or even characteristics such as sticking out ears that cause concern to the child involved.
- Explaining family trees and tracing family characteristics such as short height, or inherited characteristics such as eye colour, may cause some children anxiety about their parentage, particularly those children who are adopted, from single parent families or whose parental relationships have changed.
- The death of a family member or of a pet animal may be traumatic for some children who may need help with talking about it and coming to terms with their grief. Such children may become distressed at a later date by topics about families or animals.
- Some children may have phobias about organisms such as spiders or worms, or events such as thunderstorms and we may have to try to encourage them to look at their phobias in order to help them to overcome them.
- Children from some cultural backgrounds may be reluctant to remove clothing that is inappropriate for the activity that they are undertaking.

- Some children may have cultural or ethical objections to handling parts of animals, such as kidneys or lungs, and others may simply dislike the feel of such material.

Summary

Science can be organised as a class, group or individual activity, which the children can carry out at the same, or different, times. As there are advantages and limitations to all methods of organisation, it is beneficial to change the organisation periodically in order to choose a method that is appropriate for the science topic and our purpose. Whatever method we choose, we need to consider the ideas that the children already hold, as research indicates that the learning of science is more effective when children who hold different ideas are grouped together. We also need to consider the science concepts and skills that are to be taught and learnt, and choose activities that will support the children's learning of them by being differentiated to meet individual needs. HMI indicate that if activities are only differentiated for those children who find science hard to learn and those who learn it with ease, many children will under-achieve. Sexism and racism can also affect the teaching and learning of science, so we will have to make sure that we do not disadvantage any children by the content or the context in which we set science. We can make science accessible to all children by drawing on the rich heritage of science from a wide range of cultures and times, emphasising its relevance to our daily lives and counteracting its masculine image.

References

1 Gould C, 'Implementing National Curriculum Science – unfinished business' in *Education in Science 158,* The Association for Science Education, Hatfield, 1994, pp 8–9

2 Howe C, 'Grouping children for effective learning in science' in *Primary Science Review 13,* The Association for Science Education, Hatfield, 1990, pp 26–27

3 ASE, *Be safe! Some aspects of safety in school science and technology for key stages 1 and 2,* 2nd edition, The Association for Science Education, Hatfield, 1990

7 No-one can learn for the child

He that learns because he desires to learn will listen to the instructions he receives and apprehend their meaning.

William Godwin, *Enquiry Concerning Political Justice*, 1793

The will to learn is synonymous with the desire to gain understanding. Initially young children's ideas tend to be gained by using their senses, and are limited to objects or events in their surroundings. Thus a very young child may gain the idea that a dog has a wet tongue simply because he has experienced being licked. As the child's ideas gradually become wider ranging, one idea becomes linked to another. In this way the idea of dog may become linked to ideas about wet tongue, eating and walking. As the child gains the ability to generalise, he relates his ideas about wet tongues, eating and walking to all dogs and then to other animals. Gradually as he becomes able to relate his ideas to more abstract and less observable ones, the child becomes interested in trying to find out the reasons for things and starts to ask why and how questions, such as, "Why do animals have wet tongues?"

Children necessarily have to interpret and make sense of objects and events in terms of their own existing understandings and ideas. These understandings and ideas change with time and develop with their experiences of life. However, if the children have had only limited or similar experiences from which to develop their ideas, there is less chance that ideas from new and completely different experiences will fit in and make sense. Children whose experiences have been varied and who hold wider-ranging ideas will have more ideas that they can use to help explain new objects and events. A group of five year old children was shown a mermaid's purse (dogfish egg). Two children who had walked along beaches and explored the debris washed up by the tide recognised it, and although they did not know exactly what it was they were able to say something about it. Two other children whose experience of the seaside had been restricted to sandcastles and swimming were nonetheless able to say that it came from the sea because they recognised the smell. However, Kirsty had had no experience of the sea at all and found this inanimate looking object puzzling and could not make any sense of it. In many ways this is similar to asking the children to do an incomplete jigsaw. If they do not have enough pieces, they will not know where to fit in a new piece that we give them. Although they may know it belongs to the jigsaw and possibly which way up it goes, it will not make a great deal of sense as they cannot see where it could link to existing pieces.

Children's day-to-day activities enable them to gain ideas and to make interpretations and explanations about what they do, see and feel in order to try to understand the world around them. They are learning all the time, whether they are being taught formally or are informally seeking answers to questions that they have raised. Young children start school with many scientific ideas that they have already obtained from their daily lives. They absorb information passively, by for example watching television, listening to stories, seeing people and things at work, or actively by playing and talking to others, tasting different foods, touching different objects, doing things for themselves and so on. The way in which children use each experience depends on the ideas that they already hold. For instance, on a visit to a zoo, a young child who knows something about cats may comment on the similarities between a domestic cat and a tiger and as a result enlarge his ideas about the cat family. A child who has had little experience of cats, is less likely to compare the tiger to a cat and may simply regard the tiger as one of the many different animals seen at the zoo.

Not only do children's ideas influence the way in which they interpret their experiences, but they also influence their expectations of each experience. For example, children whose previous experiences have led them to believe that anything to do with machines is 'boring', will expect a topic about them to be equally boring and will receive new ideas and information about machines in a very different way to the child who approaches it with a more open mind.

The ideas and meanings that the children construct from their experiences will also influence their creativity. During a topic on machines two ten year old girls each designed a machine for exercising a dog. These two children worked on their ideas independently and created completely different and very individual designs. Rachel summarised hers:

You put the dog on a moving conveyor belt by opening the gate. Put a bowl of dog food at the end and turn the belt on. The dog runs one way towards the food and the belt goes the other way, so the dog keeps running but it never gets to the food.

Whereas Charis wrote:

You use a robot to take the dogs for a walk. When it's time for a walk, a bell rings and you fix the dogs to the robot. The walk lasts for half an hour. When time is up the robot stops, turns round and goes back. A clock tells the robot when to take the dogs home.

Understanding children's ideas helps us to teach science

The influence of children's existing ideas on their learning is both active and on-going. Learning is not creating ideas out of nothing, but is a linking, developing and restructuring of ideas as a result of experiences. Teaching science therefore involves providing the children with experiences that challenge their existing ideas; so that as they explore, discover, investigate and try to make sense of the world around them, they link, modify and reconstruct the ideas that they already hold. We teach science to young children in order to help them to see and act and think about objects and events, so that they are in a better position to relate scientific ideas to situations that they come across in their daily lives and to make and hold more informed decisions, judgements and opinions as a result. Thus teaching science means providing opportunities that challenge the children's existing ideas by:

- offering them new experiences in order to broaden their range of scientific ideas
- helping them to test their ideas by systematic enquiry
- helping them to make sense of new experiences and to link them to their existing ideas
- helping them to make links between ideas that they already hold but may not yet have linked together
- restructuring and developing their existing ideas and understandings in order to construct new and more scientifically acceptable meanings.

Understanding children's ideas helps us to choose appropriate learning experiences

Children's ideas influence their learning of science. We find out the ideas that the children hold so that we are better able to plan activities that challenge or extend those ideas. By challenging children's ideas we are providing them with opportunities to review what they already know and to consider whether or not their existing ideas need to change. However, challenging the children's ideas alone is insufficient. They also need opportunities to explore alternatives, if they are actively to restructure their ideas and construct new ones. The activities that we provide should encourage the children to make varied explorations and explanations.

Knowledge of children's existing ideas enables us to choose learning experiences that will help them to move towards the scientific ideas that they need and that are appropriate for them at that moment. Such knowledge also makes us aware of the point from which each child is starting in learning a particular science concept. Some children will already hold ideas that are scientific, and we need to plan activities for these children in order to help them to develop their ideas further. Other children may hold ideas that are far from scientific, or even in complete contrast to the accepted scientific view. For these children we will need to choose learning experiences that will help them replace their ideas with more scientific ones. There will also be some scientific concepts that the children have never previously had the opportunity to consider. In this case we need to plan activities that will not only provide new experiences but also help them to make links between the new ideas and the ideas that they already hold, so that they can make sense of the new information.

In a class of five year olds many of the children said that they were certain that any small object could float on water. This idea is far removed from the scientific one that an object floats on water because the weight of water displaced by the object is a force acting downwards and this downward force is equal to the upward force, or upthrust, of the water on the object. The two forces act in opposite directions. When they are equal they are balanced and so the object is able to float. When the forces are not equal, they do not balance and so the object sinks. There are other factors affecting floating and sinking, including both the density and shape of the object and the density of the liquid.

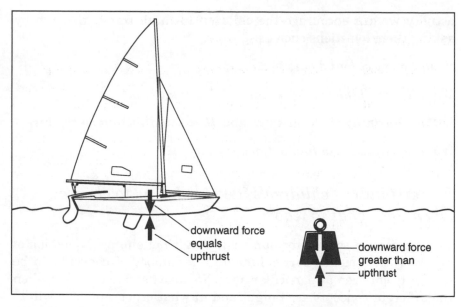

Figure 7.1 Floating and sinking

The children who thought that all small objects could float on water had their idea challenged by being provided with various sized objects that floated and were made of the same material. Once they realised that floating does not necessarily equate to size, they were encouraged to explore alternative ideas by being asked to investigate and draw conclusions about different sized and shaped objects made from a variety of materials.

Other children in the class, who already had ideas about the shape of an object and the material of which it is made affecting whether or not it floats, were given opportunities to develop ideas about the upthrust of water by suspending a number of objects in turn from an elastic band held over their finger. They were able to feel the push upwards due to water, by suspending the same object in both air and water and comparing what they felt. They were encouraged to try this in liquids of different densities so that they could begin to develop ideas about the relationship between upthrust and the density of a liquid.

We not only need to choose appropriate learning experiences that challenge the children's ideas but also to provide them with time for structured reflection. By providing 'thinking time' for the children we allow them opportunities to discuss and think about what they have done and found out, to review, modify and consolidate their ideas and to consider ways in which they can develop them further. This time has to be consciously planned, if it is to happen. At the end of an activity we can encourage the children to think things through by asking them questions such as:

What have you found out?

What do you think you have learnt from doing this?

Is there anything that you know now that you didn't know before?

What do you want to find out about next?

Understanding children's ideas helps us to choose when and what to teach

The teaching of science to young children is not simply a question of breaking the science curriculum into a number of concepts to be taught to children at particular ages. We also have to consider when the different concepts are taught and in what order, and this will to some extent be determined by the ideas that the children already hold. If, for example, we have found out that some children hold the idea that only mammals are alive, then we will need to challenge their understanding of living and non-living before introducing the idea of variety in living things, and that this includes plants, and both vertebrate and invertebrate animals.

It may also be necessary for us to put in extra steps so that the children can make sense of, develop and consolidate new ideas as they move towards more scientifically acceptable meanings. For example, to progress from an idea about forces being pushes and pulls to one that those same forces can also make things start moving, speed up, slow down or stop, requires the children to gain more understanding than may at first be apparent. A group of six year old children held the idea that after being given a push a toy car slows down "because the push's running out". A simple scientific explanation appropriate for these children is that the car slows down because the force of the 'push' is opposed by the force of friction between the car's wheels and the ground.

force of the push   force of friction

-----------▶ ◀-----------------

In order to help the children to work towards this basic scientific idea, their teacher encouraged them to explore the ideas that they already held. One child said, "I know. It'll take longer to slow down on the lino, Miss." This provided an opportunity for the children to investigate other surfaces and as a result to reflect on their existing ideas about friction. The children were then in a better position to think about friction as a force involved in slowing things down, to consider alternative explanations to their original one that the push was running out, and to move towards a more scientific understanding of opposing forces. However, their ideas about opposing forces were not fully developed by this one activity. The teacher provided further activities and experiences of opposing forces at other times and in other contexts in order to challenge the children's ideas, help them explore alternatives, and consequently modify the ideas that they held. The constructing and reconstructing of ideas in order to make sense of the world around them is necessarily a continual and progressive process for all learners.

As well as providing opportunities for the children to restructure their ideas, the learning of various scientific concepts also interacts with and enables their learning of scientific skills and attitudes. The children who systematically investigated different surfaces whilst developing ideas about friction were also able to develop ideas about fair tests, recording data, co-operation and so on. However, we need to consider when the different skills are taught and in what order, and this means we will have to take into account what the children are already able to do. For example, quantitative measurements provide more specific data than qualitative ones for the children to use when drawing conclusions. Thus "It went 53 cm on the lino and 47 cm on the tiles" gives a more definitive comparison than "It went further on the lino than the tiles" but is only possible if the children have developed measuring skills such that they can use centimetres.

Published science schemes inevitably base their texts on key science ideas. Yet even apparently simple and fundamental ideas may not be obvious to all children of the age for which the text was written. So when using a scheme we have to consider what basic scientific ideas the writer has assumed that the children will already have constructed. Then we need to ascertain whether or not the children that we are teaching do in fact hold those ideas. For example, if we find out that the children in our class have little understanding of the differences between 'keeping things warm' and 'keeping things cold', we may need to do some preparatory work before following a scheme's instructions about teaching insulation. It may also be that the order in which a scheme suggests that we teach is an inappropriate one for our children, so a scheme that is versatile is likely to be of more use to us than one that necessitates working from page 1 through to the end.

Understanding children's ideas helps us to choose the way in which we introduce activities

The way in which we ask children to carry out a task or activity can make a difference to the outcome. For example, if children know before they start, that "We're going to do an experiment to show that the polystyrene cup keeps the tea hottest", then they will undoubtedly try to show that this is what the experiment proves, even if other types of insulated cup keep the tea hotter. They are quite capable of doubting results other than the expected one, or of blaming themselves (or others) if the experiment fails to prove what they thought it would.

On the other hand, not enough guidance about an activity can leave children floundering, especially those who feel unsure about using their initiative or those who have adopted roles such as toughie in order that others do not realise that they do not know what to do. It takes time and practice before young children can organise themselves to deal with an unstructured request to "Find out which cup will keep the tea hottest". Science education can contribute to the children's overall development, if we encourage their autonomy by seeking ways in which to help them to teach themselves and each other, to learn from each other, to recognise each other's strengths and weaknesses and, at times, to make their own decisions about what, when and how they learn. By giving children the freedom to learn we put more responsibility on them than we do when we impose greater structure, and it takes time for them to adjust to this way of learning. However, the time spent in helping the children to cope with this way of learning is an investment, as the feelings of self-assertion and satisfaction that result are powerful incentives to further learning. One way in which we can begin to encourage autonomous learning is to introduce the children to planning, as this helps the children to approach investigations methodically and to start to take some responsibility for designing and carrying out activities. It is often easiest to begin by planning together as a group (figure 7.2).

As the children gain in confidence and become more prepared to make decisions for themselves, they can be introduced to a planning and recording sheet (figure 7.3). Initially they will need help with completing it, but most children quickly become able to fill it in unaided. This kind of sheet encourages the children to note what they are going to do and then what they did, and this gives them an opportunity to reflect on what they have done and found out, and to consider their findings in the light of their existing ideas. It helps them to think about any possible changes or refinements that they might want to make to their investigations, or to decide that further investigations are necessary.

What are we going to do?

We've got some things we want to sort.

We are going to try to sort them out with a magnet.

What do we think will happen?

We think all the metal things will stick to the magnet

and the things that aren't metal won't.

What equipment will we need?

We will need a magnet and the things we're going to sort.

Figure 7.2 A group of five year olds initial attempt at planning

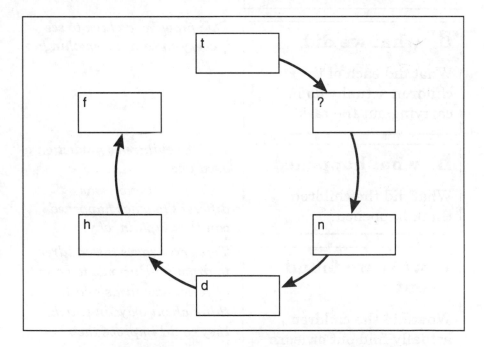

Figure 7.3 A sheet (to be enlarged) that a group of children can use for both planning and recording (see key on p. 148)

Key for Figure 7.3:

t the task What are the children being asked to do? What have they decided they are going to do?	*Phonic code for non-readers. Symbol or colour codes also help.* *Children sometimes forget or are confused about what they are supposed to be doing. This helps them check and re-focus.*
? we predict What do the children think is going to happen?	*Encourages children to think about possible outcomes, based on ideas and expectations that they already hold.*
n we need What equipment do the children think they need to carry out the task?	*Children need practice at deciding what equipment it would be appropriate to use.*
d what we did What did each of the children actually do in carrying out the task?	*This provides a check to see if every child did something.*
h what happened What did the children think happened?	*Was the children's prediction a good one?* *If their prediction was different to what happened can they explain why?*
f what we found out What did the children actually find out or learn from carrying out the task?	*This encourages the children to draw conclusions, to accept or reject new ideas and to think about ways in which they could improve their investigation.*

As a variety of approaches to science encourages different learning styles, it is not appropriate to ask children to complete this kind of sheet every time they do some science. However, with any approach we can encourage the children to be logical and creative in carrying out their activities, and to reflect on various explanations and ideas as they do so. This means that if we choose activities on work cards to challenge and extend the children's science concepts, we have to be particularly careful to consider whether or not they provide the children with opportunities to think about and use their own ideas. It is therefore important to consider whether a work card is set out in such a way that it gives the children opportunities to find answers to questions that they have raised for themselves, or simply supplies a question for the children to find an answer (or, worse, 'the right answer'). Work cards can give the children practice in following instructions, but may not encourage them to think creatively, find their own solutions or ways of tackling an activity, or construct and reconstruct their own ideas.

Summary – a teaching and learning strategy based on children's ideas

Knowledge of the ideas that the children hold about a science concept is an essential prerequisite when designing learning experiences that can be differentiated to meet the children's varied needs, build on their existing learning and are appropriate for them. Such learning experiences include:

- activities that challenge or extend the children's ideas, so that they have opportunities to review what they already know and to consider whether or not their existing ideas are still tenable.
- activities that encourage children to explore alternatives, so that they have opportunities to restructure their ideas and to construct new ones.
- activities that promote the use of ideas in a variety of situations, including new and unfamiliar ones, so that children have opportunities to transfer their learning to different contexts and become increasingly competent.
- activities that enable children to make decisions for themselves, so that they have opportunities to take responsibility for their own learning.
- time during and after activities in which children can discuss and reflect on what they have been doing and have found out, so that they have opportunities to accept or reject explanations and consolidate or restructure their ideas.

Learning experiences of this kind are essential if the children's ideas are to be challenged in order that they continue to construct and reconstruct their ideas and understandings. As their ideas develop, children will need to be provided with opportunities that enable them to explore wider-ranging, more abstract and less observable concepts, so that they can progressively link them with the ideas that they already hold and can construct new ideas. This means that as children's ideas change we will have to continue to find out what they are so that we can challenge and encourage them to develop their ideas by exploring alternatives. This way of learning is a cyclical process of finding out the children's ideas, challenging them, encouraging them to explore their existing ideas and to consider alternative explanations, to review and restructure their ideas as they see fit, to use them in new and varied situations and then to make their ideas explicit so that they can be developed further. Our task as teachers is to help each child fully to take part in this process and to accept responsibility for doing his or her own learning.

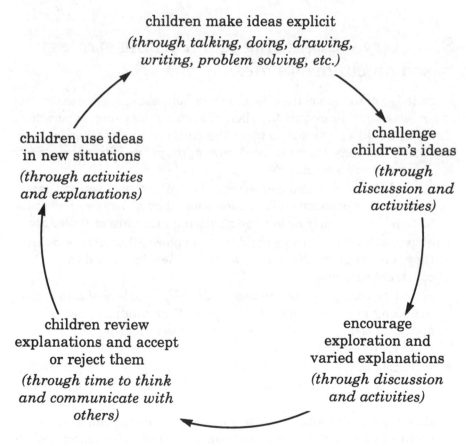

children make ideas explicit
*(through talking, doing, drawing,
writing, problem solving, etc.)*

children use ideas
in new situations
*(through activities
and explanations)*

challenge
children's ideas
*(through
discussion and
activities)*

children review
explanations and accept
or reject them
*(through time to think
and communicate with
others)*

encourage
exploration and
varied explanations
*(through discussion
and activities)*

Further reading

ASE (1991), *Questioning: an important science skill* (Association for Science Education). Many ideas for developing both teacher's and children's questioning skills.

Bell, B.F. (1981), 'When is an animal not an animal?' *J. Biol. Ed.* 15(3):213–8. Although written in 1981, is still relevant as it provides food for thought by examining students' assumption about what animals are.

Braund, M. (1990), 'Carrying out investigations' *Questions* 2(7):18–20. Discusses the advantages of, and the demands made by an investigative approach.

Browne, N. (ed) (1991), *Science and technology in the early years* (Open University Press). Describes girls' experiences of science in the early years and provides accounts of equal opportunities work done by classroom teachers.

Claxton, G. (1991), *Educating the enquiring mind* (Harvester Wheatsheaf). An enthusiastic approach to holistic learning.

Elstgeest, J. & Harlen, W. (1990), *Environmental science in the primary curriculum* (Paul Chapman Publishing). Describes examples of children investigating objects and events in order to find answers to the questions they have raised.

Farmer, M. (1994), 'Expressing their ideas' *Questions* 6(3):24–7. Describes some approaches to assessment of children's science

Farrow, S. (1994), 'Keys and classification' *Prim. Sci. Rev.* 31:12–14. Gives ideas for teaching classification and identification skills.

Gibson, H. & Towler, L. (1994), 'Using floorbooks in science investigations' *Prim. Sci. Rev.* 32:9–12. Describes rationale for, and practical examples of children using floorbooks as an aid to investigatory work.

Harlen, W. (1992), 'In defence of AT1: Scientific investigation' *Prim. Sci. Rev.* 21:2. Sets out the case for the importance of process skills in science education.

Harlen, W. & Jelly, S. (1989), *Developing science in the primary classroom* (Oliver & Boyd). Assumes no 'scientific' knowledge but supports the teacher in setting up ways in which to teach science in the classroom.

Harlen, W., Macro, C., Schilling, M., Malvern, D., & Reed, K. (1990), *Progess in primary science* (Routledge). Written as modules in order to help teachers to upgrade their skills in planning, organising, teaching and assessing science.

Hollins, M. (ed) (1984), *Science teaching in a multiethnic society*, *Vol 1* (North London Science Centre). Despite being dated, useful for someone getting to grips with these issues for the first time.

Johnsey, R. & Parkes, M. (1992), 'Learning how children learn' *Questions* 4(7):20–22. Encourages teachers to carry out small scale research in their own classrooms.

Keogh, B. & Naylor, S (1993), 'Learning in science: another way in' *Prim. Sci. Rev.* 26:22–23. Describes using cartoon as starting points and challenges to aid the development of scientific understanding.

Newton, L. (ed) 1992, *Primary science: The challenge of the 1990s* (Multilingual Matters). Collection of essays based on classroom research that explore the problems and suggest ways for teaching science.

Peacock, A. (ed) (1991), *Science in primary schools: The multicultural dimension* (Macmillan Education). Describes rationale for, and practical examples of building a multicultural dimension into teaching science.

Primary Space Project (1990 onwards), *Research reports* (Liverpool University Press). Research on understanding the development of young children's ideas in key areas of science.

Qualter, A., Strang, J., Swanton, P., & Taylor, R. (1990), *Exploration: A way of learning science* (Blackwell). Describes rationale for, and practical examples of the role of explorations in science education.

Rix, C. & Boyles, M. (1995), 'I think I know what you mean' *Prim. Sci. Rev.* 37:19–21. Classroom examples of young children's language use in science.

Russel, T. & Harlen, W. (1990), *Assessing science in the primary classroom* (Paul Chapman Publishing). Three books on assessment dealing with practical tasks, written tasks and observation.

Thorp, S. (ed) (1991), *Race, equality and science teaching* (Association for Science Education). INSET manual that addresses issues of race and equality in science teaching through focusing on classroom techniques.

Whitby, V. (1993), 'Questioning techniques used in primary science' *Prim. Sci. Rev.* 30:6–8. Compares two contrasting questioning techniques and suggests ways in which teachers can upgrade their skill when questioning children.

Wood, D. (1988), *How children think and learn* (Blackwell). Explores conflicting views about how children think and learn and how they affect children in the classroom.

Woodward, C. (1993), 'The whys and hows' *Questions* 5(7):23–4. Describes why children's questions are important and how they can be encouraged.

Woodward, C. (1993), 'So many reasons why' *Questions* 5(8):24–25. Describes how teachers' questions can contribute to children's learning in science.

Index

abstract ideas 27, 35, 44, 48,
    63-64, 66, 139, 150
acrostics 10
acting 107-109,
activities –
    everyday 2, 3, 95, 98,
    children choosing 12, 19, 23,
    stereotyping of 14,
    provided by teacher 14, 19, 21,
        24, 32, 39, 45, 55, 102-103,
        118, 125, 142, 146, 149
APU 82, 92-93, 98
artefacts 11
attitudes 21, 31, 46-49, 92, 102,
    108, 112, 145

books 9, 18, 40, 47, 80
boys and science 18-19, 93,
    132-133
brainstorming 56, 101,
burr diagram 66- 67,

card sort 103-104, 118
children working –
    in pairs 16, 19,
    alone 16, 19, 129-130
    in groups 16, 19, 81, 115-120
cinquaines 11, 134
classifying 36
classroom organisation 18,
    113-130
class work 114-115
communicating 5, 10, 81
communication 8-9, 32, 41-43,
    verbal 8, 40,
    non-verbal 8, 40, 47,

concepts 7, 16, 21, 30, 31, 43-46,
    92, 99, 117, 149
concept map 67-68, 86,
conclusions 2, 26, 34, 38, 39, 40,
    81, 84, 89,
construction toys 18, 132
contexts 23, 24, 45, 52, 60, 69, 72,
    134, 149
co-operation 13, 16, 31,
creativity 3, 13, 19, 21, 110, 111,
    116, 149
culture 47, 106, 131-132

data 37, 38, 39, 40, 81, 82,
demonstration lesson 115
describing 34, 35, 40, 42
devices for learning 26-28, 48, 49
diary 62, 76-77, 135
differentiation 102, 117, 130, 138
discussion 26, 54, 55, 56 -57, 69,
    93, 101, 114, 119
drama 107-109
drawing 60-65, 72, 73, 86, 105

embroidery 74-75
equipment 14, 19, 21, 38, 93, 129
evaluation 37, 38, 40, 111
    of learning 67, 72, 86-89, 92, 94
evidence of learning 72-86, 94,
experiences of science –
    pre-school 3, 26,
    informal 3-4, 5-12, 14-17, 50
    formal 24-26, 30-31, 50
experiment 8, 38, 146
explanations 3, 40, 42
exploration 13, 15